WIELICZKA

Marian Hanik

WIELICZKA

Seven Centuries of Polish Salt

with photographs by
Stanisław Klimowski

Interpress Publishers
Warsaw

ISBN 83-223-2231-3

Contents

MONEY AND POLITICS   7

Royal Monopoly   7

The Wealth of Old Poland   9

The Oldest State-owned Company   10

Bankers and Athletes   13

Palaces of Salt   14

How to Make Money?   16

The Lubomirski Saga Continued   19

Saxon Management   20

Under Foreign Rule   21

Merchants and the Salt Black Market   23

TECHNOLOGY   27

From a Salt-works to a... Salt-works   28

Queen Kinga's Ring   33

The Adventure Down the Shoemaker's Well   35

The Sad Lot of the Bochnia Salt Mine   37

The Opening of Mountains   39

How a Digger Hewed Salt   43

Dogs, Horses and Treadmills   44

The Wet Enemy   45

The Supporting of the Firmament   47

Fire, Vapours and Saltpetre   48

MEN   50

Miners of His Royal Majesty   51

Diggers and Bearers   52

"Exposed to a Certain Death..."   56

Rebels   58

He and the White Lady   59

Mining Families   62

Tourist Attractions   66

Treatment of Dissipated   69

The Professor   71

PROSPECTS   72

*The authors would like to thank the historians Jerzy Grzesiowski
and Józef Piotrowicz of the Museum of the Cracow Salt Mines;
Ignacy Markowski, managing director of the Wieliczka Salt Mine;
the engineers Jerzy Lachman, Janusz Wójcik and Janusz Wiewiórka;
as well as Stanisław Cholewa who took us the old mine,
for help and kindness without which the present book
could not have come into being.*

Money and Politics

Human attitudes to the riches of nature change in mysterious ways. Our ancestors would probably be surprised to hear that fresh air and clear water could be precious and protected commodities. They would be no less surprised to see cheap salt generally available. This is what one should bear in mind talking about the ancient salt mine at Wieliczka. Familiarity with the geological structure of the Earth and modern drilling methods have made salt abundant these days. Actually, it is hard to believe that in the past the value of salt was equal to that of the most precious metals. And so, earnings from the Wieliczka mine for a number of centuries used to be a major pillar of the Polish economy and contributed greatly to the might of this country. It was due to salt that Wawel castle, the Renaissance residence of Polish kings, could be built. Money earned from salt also paid for the erection of a number of magnificent palaces and fine burghers' houses in the Cracow Market Square. It was salt, too, that paid for the upkeep of Poland's oldest university. "Wieliczka gold" was used to cover soldiers' pay and poets' royalties. The miners' salty sweat adorned the interiors of castles and churches with works of art. Wieliczka, now a Greater Cracow suburb, was in the past the target of armed incursions as well as a subject of diplomatic wrangling. Huge sums of money were at stake and Wieliczka was a focal point in national and international politics.

In the Middle Ages, salt was covered by the royal mining privileges, under which all subterranean deposits as well as brine sources on the surface were the property of the monarch. Prospecting for and excavation of minerals could only be undertaken with a licence known as a "miner's charter" or in German as "*Bergrecht*". The licence was granted by the duke. Those who received such a privilege financed the entire undertaking and ran the full risk. If a licensee discovered a salt deposit, he organized exploitation and marketing. In exchange, the duke deducted a definite part of production. Those principles governed mining throughout medieval Europe, including Poland. Things were different in the case of the exploitation of brine sources. Prior to the discovery of rock salt deposits, salt was obtained by evaporation of water from surface brine sources. We shall return to that particular method of salt making further in the book.

A number of surviving documents in which the duke authorized magnates or religious houses to receive salt free of charge, show that in the 12th century such a gift took two forms. Either processed salt was received (which means that the duke owned salt-works) or the donatee was given a definite amount of mineral and enjoyed the right to process it in his own salt-works and sometimes to sell surplus salt at a precisely defined place and time (e.g. once a week, at the market, at the inn etc.). Therefore, it seems that the monarch was not only entitled to mine salt like other minerals, but also to process and sell it.

In subsequent centuries, the history of the royal mining privilege confirmed a tendency for salt production to become a monopoly in the hands of the duke. In the mining of minerals the duke increasingly relinquished his right to a percentage of earnings, giving licences for free mining (this usually concerned the owners of land rich in mineral deposits). Successive rulers of the Little Poland province around Cracow lavished salt-mining licences on their subjects, which

ROYAL MONOPOLY

7

substantially decreased their incomes, but they did not relinquish their hold on salt production and marketing.

In 1251, deposits of rock salt were found at Bochnia. The ruling duke Boleslaus the Chaste did not take long to react: in the 1270s he issued a document annulling all previous licences. In this way, all mineral deposits and means of production became the sole possession of the ruler. That radical step must have caused considerable protest (mainly on the part of the Church, which had previously enjoyed a majority of the licences). To offset the dissatisfaction, the duke awarded compensation to a number of former licensees in the form of an hereditary allowance of money and salt. Some of the salt mines were encumbered with these payments in cash and kind until 1772 *. However, no landowner ever became a shareholder in brine sources, salt-works and mines. Joachim Vadian, the Swiss humanist and chancellor of Vienna University, wrote in the 16th century: "In a number of places in Sarmatia, traces of salt are very much in evidence. However, the law forbids those who live nearby to mine it so that its value should not diminish".

In the first period of the functioning of the Cracow salt mines the king was forced to avail himself of the services of private entrepreneurs. The reason was the enormous cost of mining investment as well as the need to recruit workers adept at working the mines. The rules governing the admission of private capital were very different from regulations governing the mining of other minerals. An entrepreneur ran the entire risk of prospecting and drilling. However, if a salt deposit was found, it became the king's property and fell under his management. The monarch returned the cost in instalments and guaranteed an hereditary allowance, with the right to mine a definite amount of salt once only. The prospector was appointed technical supervisor in the administration of the mine. Records exist of one such contract concluded in 1334 between King Casimir the Great and three Wieliczka burghers: Heink the son of Wilhelm, Heink the son of Paulin and Jaśko Jelitka. As of the 15th century, royal salt mines financed their investments from their own resources.

Similar regulations protecting the royal monopoly were binding for everyone wishing to prospect for salt deposits. Such attempts were made in the 14th century at Tuchów by the Benedictines of Tyniec, on the Dunajec River by the Cracow castellan Spycimir as well as in the 16th century at Rabka. All of them ended in failure.

What made the first rulers of Poland so consistently and determinedly struggle for their exclusive rights to supply salt to the country? The fact that salt is a vital necessity and man cannot do without it was decisive. It should be remembered that before the advent of the epoch of refrigerators and freezers, large quantities of salt were used to preserve meat, butter, fish, cheese, for the purposes of food-processing, tanning, gunpowder manufacture as well as for the production of alum, glass etc. The 16th century poet Adam Schroeter wrote that one simply cannot do without salt, which is used to season meals, prevents rotting and mouldering in nature, protects man against cancer, plague, ulcers etc.

Salt was vital to each and every inhabitant of Poland, irrespective of his social status or background. Thus, salt production was not only a source of income as in the case of other minerals, but was also a major instrument of power. Boleslaus the Chaste appreciated the fact and nationalized the entire salt indus-

* In 1772 Wieliczka fell into Austrian hands following the first partition of Poland — translator's note.

try in Poland in one decisive move. His successors did not let this precious possesion slip away from them. They controlled salt mining to such an extent that even the abolition of the royal mining privilege did not manage to subvert their monopoly. Legislation abolishing the privilege was passed by the Seym (Parliament) in 1573 when the gentry demanded the right to mine all minerals within their estates. The right was secured by the *pacta conventa* each of the Polish monarchs elected to the throne had to sign. Salt mines in the Cracow province and salt-panning works in Rus, practically the only salt-producing centres in Poland, were then owned by the king. In 1590 when the income of the monarch was separated from the Treasury, salt mines and salt-panning works were included in estates at the exclusive disposal of the king. The only attempt to break the monopoly was made in the 17th century by the Lubomirski family. Taking advantage of the abolition of the royal mining privilege, they opened a private mine within their estate near Wieliczka. We shall return to this question later on in the book.

THE WEALTH OF OLD POLAND

"There are untold deposits of salt in Sarmatia [Old Poland]. Other, distant peoples also use the salt, which is a source of the country's hefty profit," wrote Hartmann Schedel in his *Chronicon Mundi*, published in 1495 in Nuremberg. That "hefty profit" was also underscored by each and every author of descriptions of the Wieliczka mine. In the 16th century, Vadian wrote: "The Polish ruler draws a more sizeable income from that source of wealth than others could extract from the richest gold and silver mines." Bernardo Bongiovanni was more specific in his account dating back to 1560: "The Polish king primarily earns his income from salt. After expenses are deducted, 106,000 thalers a year are left. Excise taxes amount to 52,000 thalers...". King Casimir the Jagiellon himself admitted that the mines at Wieliczka and Bochnia accounted for such a substantial part of the kingdom's budget that it would be a shame if they were to suffer losses.

In the 14th century, the salt mines provided a third of the income of the Treasury. The rulers used the money to pay regular allowances to their spouses, members of the royal family as well as to officials occupying various state posts. The mines also paid for the upkeep of the royal court, charioteers, musicians, apothecaries and doctors. They were also obliged to supply food, to maintain royal horses etc. The garrisons manning castles defending trade routes as well as individuals who had served the country particularly well received salt free of charge.

Cracow Academy owes a lot to salt. Its original founder, King Casimir the Great, financed the entire new university from income generated by the salt mine. His successors as well as Polish magnates lavished donations and endowments on the university. King Sigismund the Old, for instance, presented ten lumps of salt to students of the Hungarian Dormitory in 1510, while Bishop Andrzej Noskowski of Płock endowed the Philosophers' Dormitory with his allowance from the Wieliczka salt mine. Salt mines were the source of money for the reconstruction of the Wawel castle under King Sigismund the Old and his son. That was where money came from for royal patronage of the arts and sciences (endowments from Cracow salt mines were received by the writers Marcin Kromer and Andrzej Frycz Modrzewski, poets Jan Kochanowski and Wespazjan Kochowski, the painter Tommaso Dolabella as well as the architect Giovanni Trevano. Numerous financial obligations of the mines resulted from royal endowments on churches, monasteries, parishes, hospitals etc. All of these substantially decreased the king's income. Therefore, they were periodically subject to verification, when an attempt was made to cut the number of annuities, both in cash and kind.

A new form of financial obligation emerged. It was known as "Lenten salt". Under the Nieszawa Statute of 1454, King Casimir the Jagiellon allowed the gentry from the Little Poland province to buy salt directly at the mine without the need to use the services of trading burghers. Additionally, the king exempted the transport of such salt from excise tax. The gentry were to collect the salt three times a year during Lent. Soon the privilege was extended to cover all Poland. Initially, the Treasury did not lose much, but as time went by, production costs went up and the gentry fiercely opposed price rises. In the mid-17th century the cost of extracting a lump of salt was four times higher than the price paid for it by those of "noble birth". The gentry were determined to insist on the privilege: suffice it to say that minor noblemen from the Kuyavy region made it clear at a regional diet meeting in 1675 that they "would be more willing to defend the country" if they received their overdue supplies of salt.

Therefore, it seems that the Cracow salt mines must have produced a huge profit to shoulder such financial burdens. In fact, the mines often came to the rescue of the Treasury offering generous loans on security. In this way, for instance, King John Casimir paid for Austrian assistance in fighting the Swedes in the mid-17th century.

THE OLDEST STATE-OWNED COMPANY

The fact that salt deposits were the sole property of Poland's early rulers gave rise to a number of management problems that could not be resolved with the use of management patterns common in the mining of minerals in the West. Thus, during the first century of the Wieliczka and Bochnia mines new, unique structures of organization were developed. The effect of that century was the formation of Poland's oldest state-owned company known as the Cracow salt mines, which has been in operation until present day. The company featured such modern characteristics as hired labour (usually paid upon tut), centralization and highly developed division of labour, which is remarkable considering that it was introduced in the mid-14th century. The final rules of operation of the company were developed under King Casimir the Great. To put an end to controversies about who was responsible for what at the mine, the king ordered the mine workers to testify under oath before the royal council. The hearing concerned the customary spheres of responsibility. Using the protocol of the meeting, the Treasurer Dymitr of Klecie drafted a list of regulations which was approved by the king and was enacted as a parliamentary statute.

The Casimir Statute opens with a list of royal council members and another one including the miners who testified before that body. Other parts of the document define the rights and responsibilities of particular officials and groups of workers, the way accounts should be conducted between the mine and the Treasury. A list of wages is given as well as prices at which salt was sold. An appendix contains updated lists of wages. We shall be returning to the statute passed by King Casimir the Great since rules governing the operation of the mines remained unchanged, with only slight alterations, until the early 18th century.

The royal company consisted of mines and salt-works at Wieliczka and Bochnia, ports handling salt on the Vistula River as well as another salt-works at Dobiegniew, which started its operation in the 17th century. The company was managed by an official appointed by the king. The weakening of royal power was the reason why this responsibility was transferred to the Seym

10

(Parliament) in the mid-15th century. The head of the company was not subject to the jurisdiction of the starost * and was accountable directly to the king, enjoying his special protection. King Ladislaus Jagiełło issued an order to the starosts in 1425 under which they were obliged to protect salt-mine masters and shield them from acts of violence whenever the masters might find themselves under threat. He also authorized the starosts to punish all those who wronged or insulted the mine masters. Punishment was to depend on the nature of the offence. The monarchs cared so much for the masters that they even protected them against the intrusiveness of the high-ranking officials who frequented Wieliczka out of curiosity and desire for a lavish reception. The first such case was described in the statute passed by King Casimir the Great. Neorza, the voivode, arrived at the mine and ordered breakfast to be brought for him. Upon learning about this, the king became so annoyed at the voivode that it took several months for the courtiers to succeed in pleading with the king to forgive the official. However, the king forbade unauthorized persons to visit his company. Those who disobeyed the ban faced the confiscation of property or even death. "When magnates visit the mine," the statute said, "the mine master is unable to mind the king's interests if he has to entertain guests."

It seems that visitors posed a serious problem since further instructions were issued, all of them including the ban, though with briefer wording. In 1592 the masters of the Bochnia mine were forbidden to entertain guests at the mine under the king's personal order, since the monarch "did not wish his home to be transformed into an inn".

The mine master administered the company either as a royal official receiving an annuity ("*ad fideles manus*") or as a lease-holder. The salt mines were too precious a possession, however, to be leased like other estates. Thus, relevant contracts substantially restricted the right of the lease-holder, which enabled the king to keep an eye on the running of the mine. The lease-holder annually paid a sum of money specified in the contract into the Treasury, incurred all production costs and was responsible for the distribution of "Lenten salt", allowances and annuities according to a list approved by the king. The contract imposed strict restrictions on the volume of production, specifying what amount of a particular kind of salt was to be mined annually. This prevented the deposits from wasteful exploitation.

The authority of the mine master was restricted by the rights of the Cracow chamberlain and technical manager. Both of them represented the interests of the king and controlled to some extent the operation of the mine. The chamberlain had no right to interfere with the mine's economic policies, but was obliged to inform the king about dangers posed to the mine and to prosecute those who were engaged in the illegal salt trade. The chamberlain was also in charge of a tribunal which dealt with strikers, saboteurs and miners engaged in mutinies. The tribunal also heard complaints of miners. Violations of work discipline fell under the jurisdiction of the mine master. The technical manager was responsible for prospecting for fresh salt deposits and maintenance work. In this area of responsibilities, he was to a large extent independent of the mine master since he was accountable directly to the king for the technical state of the mine.

Relations among mine masters, the Cracow chamberlain and technical managers were usually in poor shape. Mine masters were reluctant to accept the fact that someone else was keeping an eye on them, so they constantly

---

* Officer in charge of a district — translator's note.

11

strove to limit the respective spheres of responsibility of the chamberlain and the technical manager. The role of the chamberlain was successfully eliminated in the 17th century, while the technical managers became less influential in the early 18th century when the Saxon dynasty that acceded to the Polish throne installed their supporters in key administrative posts.

The king exercised control over the salt mines mainly through a specially appointed commission. Initially, it was sent to Wieliczka and Bochnia when a new mine master was installed. Its job was to do the stock-taking and draft an inventory. The commission might also verify a person's right to an endowment in cash or kind. A large-scale operation of this kind took place in 1507. Following devastation caused by mismanagement on the part of several lease-holders, the king decided at a Seym session in 1588 to send commissioners to Wieliczka and Bochnia every two years to see how the master was coping with his job. Each time, the commission was appointed by the king from among high-ranking civil servants and deputies to the Seym. The commission included the technical manager and a representative of the chamberlain's office. The commissioners checked the shape of underground galleries, overground buildings and salt-works. The mine master was obliged to account for the payment of allowances. In cases of "*ad fideles manus*" mining, a careful check of books was also made. The commissioners drafted a detailed description of their activities. The report included a number of recommendations that were submitted to the king for acceptance and then sent to the mine as instructions.

In the 16th century, the Cracow salt mines were among the largest companies in Europe. Apart from actual miners and managerial staff, the mines also employed carpenters, coopers, blacksmiths, drivers, stable-boys, watchmen and servants. The pay-roll included in the statute passed by King Casimir the Great lists "a worker who washes dishes", "a maid who lays the table", and a forester, to mention but a few. For a time the mines ran their own "canteens" for mine workers, waggoners and officials. A physician was also on the staff of the mine. A system of "social security" and "pensions" was also developed. The fact that the company was state-owned forced managers to keep detailed records, including account books, stock-taking reports as well as notes from weekly board meetings. Protocols drafted by royal commissions were scrupulously kept and written instructions were published. A sizeable part of that material has survived to the present day. It is a rich source of information, often exceeding the scope of mining technologies. From lists of catering expenses, for instance, the daily menu of our ancestors can be re-created. It turns out that in the mid-16th century the amount of vegetables and seasonings consumed by the "canteen" was steadily on the rise, which is clearly a reflection

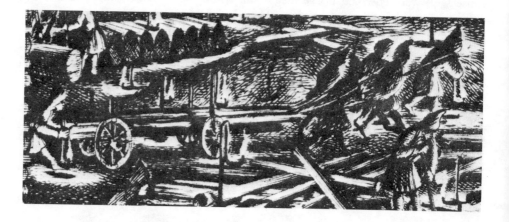

of Italian influences. Reports and instructions drafted by royal commissions offer a wealth of detail concerning customs and beliefs that were widespread among Wieliczka miners.

The operation of the royal company at Wieliczka ended in 1772 following the first partition of Poland. The organizational model going back to the times of King Casimir the Great was changed by the Austrian management. However, before we take up the subject of the mine's operation under the Austrian empire, let us pause for a moment to take a look at several prominent mine masters. These included a couple of outstanding characters, some of whom have come down in history due to their positive features, others due to their notoriety.

Little is known about early mine masters. We know their names from signatures on documents, some of which are not related to Wieliczka, where a "supparius", or the one who manages the mines, figures among other posts.

In Later period, the position was usually occupied by wealthy merchants of German or Italian origin. The first Italian master mentioned by name was Paulinus Cavallo of Genoa who was in charge of the mines from 1346. Mine masters were usually closely connected with the Treasury since the lease of the mines was a security against generous loans offered to the monarch. Some of the managers held posts corresponding to those of modern "finance ministers", though the title of the Treasurer was reserved for persons of noble birth. Such a position was for instance occupied by Mikołaj Wierzynek, Cracow's mayor who managed the mines in the years 1366—68 and who gave a memorable reception during a meeting of monarchs in 1364.

Prior to that, in 1336, the mine master's father Mikołaj Sr. was appointed officer at Wieliczka. This was a period of spectacular development for the town. King Casimir the Great ordered a defensive wall to be erected around Wieliczka and expanded the castle there. It is worth taking a closer look at the latter building since it was one of a few structures erected specially to defend industrial facilities. Its origins probably date back to the foundation of Wieliczka in 1298 under Henry IV Probus, a privilege that was confirmed in 1299 by Przemysł II. The castle was the seat of salt-mining administration. It also held what apparently were salt-storage facilities as well as barracks for army troops. King Casimir the Great commissioned the reconstruction of the main body of the castle, transforming it into a representative residence of the mine master. During the alterations, a kitchen building was also put up.

Another mine master, Mikołaj Bochner, was also a wealthy Cracow burgher. He apparently had a special feel for mining since he also leased lead mines at Olkusz and Chęciny. He was appointed to the post in 1402 by King Ladislaus Jagiello and carried out his responsibilities diligently. He introduced a number of technological innovations and drilled a new well at Bochnia. The well is now known under his name. That particular project proved to be Bochner's undoing. He went bankrupt and was jailed for debts.

The 15th century was not a particularly profitable period for the Cracow salt mines. The burden of new annuities, allowances and endowments increased (King Ladislaus Jagiello, newly converted to Christianity, proved to be particularly generous in his gifts to the Church). The *ad fideles manus* management was at that time practically non-existent. The mines were constantly mortgaged for sizeable loans in cash, which were used to finance wars and active dynastic policies. Mine masters changed quite often. They were interested in accumulating their own capital as fast as they could and investing it in land. The diminishing authority of the king made the appointment of a mine master the responsibility of the Seym. Increasingly, wealthy noblemen were appointed to the post, though rich merchants, including a number of Italians, such as Pietro Picarani of Venice, Antonio and Leonardo Medici as well as Arnoldo Tedaldi, were a majority. Typical economic activities of those times were conducted by Mikołaj Serafin in the 1440s. He dynamically penetrated markets in Silesia, considerably increased output with the use of new ideas in mine transport and expansion of galleries. It was thanks to him that a new well, known as "Seraf", was commissioned. It was the last well to be drilled by private investors. The master invested in a way that guaranteed early profit, but he neglected labour security precautions, which caused collapse or flooding of particular galleries.

Sometimes, however, the appointment of a mine master was not caused by the state of the Treasury or other major reasons. According to early 16th century chroniclers, during a visit to Wieliczka by King Alexander, a Jan Jordan clad in armour and full soldier's kit, jumped across the opening of the wall in honour of the monarch. Grateful for that sporting feat, the king appointed Jordan mine master. Incidentally, this is perhaps the first news of a Polish athlete's profit from a successful jump...

PALACES OF SALT

A period of spectacular development for the mines began under the management of treasurer Andrzej Kościelecki, though his personal contribution, as we are about to discover, was rather insignificant. Kościelecki became famous due to his exceptional courage and selflessness. Jost Ludwik Decjusz, secretary to King Sigismund the Old, wrote in 1510 that a wicked miner set fire to props in an underground cave, which started a major conflagration. Chambers and galleries filled with smoke and a number of miners were lost searching for an exit. In the resulting melée, several miners were trampled to death or died of suffocation. It was then that Andrzej Kościelecki decided to go to the miners' rescue, though no one else dared to go down into the smoke. He ordered others to tie him to a rope and lower him down the shaft. He was accompanied by Seweryn Betman, a foreman and Cracow councillor. Betman was nearly ninety, his hair was grey and it was he who rescued the mine master, Kościelecki having passed out in the smoke. Thanks to the remarkable feat of the two daring men, the fire was put out and the galleries were saved from danger.

At the time when Andrzej Kościelecki was the mine master (1507—15) the operation of the mines was greatly influenced by a man who deserves more than just a passing mention.

His name was Jan Boner. He arrived in Cracow from Landau in 1483 and was given rights of citizenship. Three years later he established a company that dealt in trade, catering, lease of customs houses and money-lending. (One of his partners was Seweryn Betman who was later to accompany Kościelecki on his fateful descent to the blazing mine.) Boner's huge capital, extensive contacts throughout Europe and what would be termed today as businessman's flair, helped to make him a monopolist in supplies to the state. He also made the Treasury dependent on him due to sizeable loans. His diligence, talent and genuine loyalty to his new homeland were the reason why Boner was appointed financial adviser to the court. It was he and not the nominal treasurer Andrzej Kościelecki, and later Mikołaj Szydłowiecki, who managed the Treasury. During the early reign of King Sigismund the Old, he saved the country when he paid outstanding soldier's pay to the army. Boner literally paid for the upkeep of the court (naturally, against further securities). He became a truly

14

indispensable person. He not only financed, but actually organized the king's wedding ceremonies, first to Barbara Zapolya and then to Bona Sforza. In 1522, the king owed Boner 150,000 florins, while the annual income of the Treasury amounted to a mere 29,000 florins.

Boner showed interest in the salt mines, a significant source of money as they were, at a very early period. It was on his advice (and for the money he lent the king) that the monarch took the mines out of pledge and introduced "*ad fideles manus*" management. Until the 1580s the mines were under the direct control of the royal administration.

The year 1515 saw the death of Andrzej Kościelecki and Jan Boner was appointed the mines' master. He ordered Stanisław Tarnowski of Nieszawa, the scribe of the Wieliczka mine, to draft a detailed inventory of the entire company. His next moves included streamlining mine operations, linking wages to productivity and introducing new regulations for the managerial staff. He also developed trade, built several ports along the banks of the Vistula river and streamlined the transport of salt by water. His management marked a period of rapid and harmonious development of the mine.

Jan Boner died on 15 December 1523 leaving no successors. His estate and posts (including the management of the salt mines) were inherited by his nephew Seweryn. The new master was less of a banker than his uncle and focused on the arts. In fact, both of them were surrounded by the most outstanding artists of that date, who spread the word of the mighty and magnificent royal salt mines near Cracow. In his account of the Wieliczka and Bochnia mines, Joachim Vadian described Jan Boner as follows: "He is a man of remarkable dignity and wisdom. He is second to no one at the court of King Sigismund in terms of rank and prestige. Boner is the first foreigner (born on the Rhine) who won such riches and honours from the rulers of Poland." Jodok Willich of Reszel, a prominent physician dedicated his account of the Cracow salt mines to "The honourable Seweryn Boner of Balice, starost of Biecz, master of the salt mines of the Kingdom of Poland etc."

Seweryn Boner lavished a truly royal gift upon his staff: in 1534 he endowed the miners' guild with a representative coat-of-arms in the form of a horn covered with silver. This masterpiece of Renaissance goldsmithery was probably made by Andreas Dürer, a brother of Albrecht, the renowned painter. The horn later went through some rather sensational adventures. In 1874 it was stolen by Karol Leo, the son of a mine master, who sold it to a Vienna antiquarian for a mere 290 Austrian florins. In Vienna, the horn was bought for all of 2,400 florins by Anselm Samuel Rothschild, an art collector. Persistent efforts on the part of the mine management that lasted a number of years, culminated in the recovery of this gem from Nathaniel Rothschild, the son of the purchaser. At present, the magnificent gift of Seweryn Boner takes pride of place among the exhibits of the underground museum.

The period when the mine was managed by the Boner family was marked not only by a flourishing development of the mine itself, but also of the town. Wieliczka became one of the largest centres of Little Poland. It had a water supply system, two hospitals, a bath-house and an opulent parish church. The Boners were also determined to make their official residence an imposing building. And so, the mine castle underwent thorough reconstruction. Valuable objects were added to its collection. It had a hall where twenty-four paintings were shown, all of them of former mine masters. Other rooms were adorned with the portraits of kings, royal coats-of-arms, the latter to be found also on glass. (Window panes were a luxury at that time.)

15

The town quickly accumulated wealth due to the favourable development of the mine. However, the mine started to put the squeeze on the town. Only low and wooden houses were put up, apparently in order not to put too much strain on the ground. Small wonder then that each time fire broke out it spread rapidly and the loss of life was heavy. On 23 October 1535 mine buildings were spared by fire, but almost the entire town was burnt to the ground. Twenty-one years later, a major conflagration was reported in Wieliczka again. This time wooden structures above the shafts as well as storage facilities where barrels were kept, caught fire. Spatial development of the mine caused more and more frequent cave-ins. One of the most tragic disasters was on 18 May 1582 when the roof of the "Małdrzyk" chamber collapsed. The tremor damaged 25 houses, some of which actually fell inside the mine.

The 1582 disaster is evidence of a rapid deterioration of the mine, which had been apparent for several years. The good times of the Boners are a thing of the past. The management of two of their successors, Spytko of Tarnów and Hieronim Bużeński, marked the end of the royal administration that had lasted since the beginning of the 16th century. The management of lease-holders (which never augured well for the mines) was started by a Prospero Provana in 1577. He was an enterprising, though unscrupulous man who only seemed interested in his own business. Records show, for instance, that he closed salt-works towers at Wieliczka and transferred their equipment to his private salt-works. It is worth mentioning, though, that Poland owes her first postal line to Provana. The line opened in 1558 under a royal licence, connecting Cracow and Italy. The ancient postal system seems to have worked more efficiently than present-day services: it only took three days and a half for a letter to reach Vienna from Cracow.

HOW TO MAKE MONEY?

The 1580s marked a turning point in the history of Cracow mine masters. Until then, the post had been occupied mainly by wealthy burghers who were connected with the Treasury in one way or another. True, there was no lack of unscrupulous money-lenders among them who amassed great riches at the expense of the royal salt mines. However, there were also those, like the Boners, who realized that their business could only flourish in a wealthy and stable state and that favourable development of the mines was in the long run also in their own interest. In the late 16th century the gentry and magnates predominated among the mine masters. Meanwhile, an epoch started when kings were elected to the throne and when Poland, until recently a major power with a decisive say in this part of Europe, became nothing more than a card in European politics. The fate of the country was soon to hinge on particular, selfish interests of powerful magnate families, for whom patriotism became and the love of motherland were but empty slogans.

The Lubomirskis were a case in point. The grandfather was a petty nobleman, but his grandson was to be involved in political schemes with foreign powers, spark off a civil war and waste the chances of reforms in Poland.

Sebastian Lubomirski became the lease-holder of the salt mines near Cracow in 1581. Within months, Cracow merchants started complaining that the mine master made it difficult for them to buy salt. Lubomirski did not take long to react. According to another complaint, written a year later, the lease-holder, together with his servants, ravaged the countryside, held up carts leaving Wieliczka and robbed the merchants of salt. It was also reported that he sold blocks of salt that were four times smaller than the required size, which apparently did not do any good to the reputation of the royal company, previously renowned for its trustworthiness. Finally, rumours started circulating that Lubomirski was himself engaged in the salt trade, which was an offense under the statute passed by King Casimir the Great, a regulation no one had dared to violate before. Protests were also lodged by the salt-works owners in Toruń, the Loiss family, who mined salt at Wieliczka from their own well and floated it down the Vistula river. Lubomirski closed their well, laid off the miners who had worked it and sunk barges loaded with salt. This was actually an attempt to eliminate competitors since in 1583 he became the owner of a private salt-works at Toruń. He also pursued a very consistent policy vis à vis the Treasury. He fell behind in payments, charged sums of money for maintenance work that was never done and actually did not consider it to be below his dignity to steal mine timber. Lubomirski cut miners' wages, sparking off a wave of protest and strikes. All of them were brutally suppressed. Following a hearing at a Cracow court in 1583, it was recorded that miners from Bochnia demonstrated serious wounds. A Mikołaj Sagan had his face slashed and his body seriously wounded. There was also a wound on his shoulder-blade. A Wojciech Dębosz had been wounded with a shot from a harquebus, while another miner Wojciech Zielonka had had his leg shot through. A Jan Mniszek testified that he was abducted and tied up in front of the inn and was then taken to Wiśnicz, Lubomirski's castle, where he was locked in a tower and whipped. A year later, desperate miners at Bochnia laid siege to the master's castle. Lubomirski managed to get away through the window. Another strike broke out in 1590. The Cracow chamberlain had to step in to mediate, but he decided in the miners' favour.

The way Lubomirski managed the mines was soon bound to affect their condition. Alarming reports were written by royal commissioners. At a Seym session in 1585 the gentry demanded that the mines be not leased in view of damage done to this vital company by the lease-holders, and its impact on the country. However, Lubomirski was reluctant to quit his lucrative position. In 1592 royal commissioners virtually had to use force to evict him. The condition of the mine is best evident in the fact that over the following three years Wieliczka had to spend 12,000 zlotys a year on maintenance work compared to the 2,000 or so Lubomirski had spent on the purpose annually.

Sebastian Lubomirski did not disappear from the scene for long. Only a decade or so later he returned to the trade — this time as the owner of the Lednica mine that bordered on Wieliczka. He soon shifted border markings delimiting the royal hold and put up a private well known as "Lubomierz" on

this enlarged plot of land. Formally, the management of the mines had no right to prevent him from doing so since the royal privilege had been abolished in 1576. However, concern about the royal monopoly prompted energetic efforts to buy Lednica. The transaction materialized. In return for Lednica, Lubomirski acquired ten villages, including Mszana Dolna, Poręba and Niedź-wiedź. The contract was drafted in 1607. In the same year, Lubomirski became the lease-holder of the Bochnia salt mine. This was one of a few cases of a person leasing just one of the mines.

Sebastian Lubomirski died in 1613. At the time when he became the lease-holder of the salt mines in 1581 he owned the two villages of Sławkowice and Sułów. Within thirty-two years his estate expanded to include the castles of Biecz and Wojnicz, the districts of Dobczyce, Sącz, Spisz, Lipnica and Sando-mierz. He also bought the Wiśnicz estate from the Kmita family, together with a castle. Lubomirski had an imposing Spisz Palace in the Cracow Market Square built, restored a number of castles at Lubowla and in the Spisz region. He also bought the title of count of the Holy Roman Empire from the Emperor Rudolf II. A popular saying circulated among the gentry at that time, linking Lubomirski's wealth to his grip on the salt mining and salt trade. An allusion to the Lubomirskis was also made by Stefan Czarniecki, a prominent military commander, who compared his own patriotic motives to the greediness and selfishness of the magnate.

However, this did not mark the end of the family's connection with the salt mines near Cracow. Stanisław, Sebastian's son, appeared to be a heir worthy of his father since he started a competition with the Wieliczka mine that was to last for a century. Before we focus on the man, it might be worthwhile describing the epoch in which he lived and worked.

The worsening political situation in Poland, the greediness of mine masters, the devastation of the mines and squalid living conditions of the miners, combined to bring about a rapid economic decline of Wieliczka and the depravity of its inhabitants. Starvation wages made theft the only means of survival. Thus, the city was transformed into a huge market of stolen salt. No respect for the law, the impunity of mine officials and the bloody suppression of strikes further aggravated the social situation, already worsened by religious conflicts. In the late 16th century the influence of the Reformation on Wieliczka was considerable (the mine master Hieronim Bużeński was a devout Calvinist). A reaction to this was the erection of new churches, including the wooden St. Sebastian's church consecreated in 1598 that has survived until present times, and the arrival of the Jesuits and the Reformati Order. History did not spare Wieliczka from devastation. In 1587 the town was looted by the troops of Archduke Maximilian who was fighting for the Polish throne. Once again, Wieliczka was plundered in 1613 by former soldiers of the Moscow campaign who had received no pay.

Ominous signs of tragedies to come were very much in evidence. In the 1647—49 period the salt mines were leased by Hieronim Radziejowski, then the Łomża starost. As a vice-chancellor of the Crown, Radziejowski was sentenced by court martial to exile. He escaped to Stockholm and used it as a base for fomenting magnate opposition in Poland, in preparation for the Swedish invasion. The next mine master was Jan Weihardt Wrzeszczowicz who left Wieliczka in 1651. He returned there again four years later, this time as major general of Charles Gustavus' troops. The figure of the traitor was immortalized by Henryk Sienkiewicz in his novel *The Deluge*. He was the infamous adviser of General Müller during the siege of the Jasna Góra shrine.

18

It was also Wrzeszczowicz who brought the Swedes over to Wieliczka. Swedish troops burnt down the town, levelled the defensive walls and looted the mine. Two years after the Swedish raid, in 1657, Wieliczka was once again plundered by their allies — the troops of the Transylvanian duke György Rákóczy. A further two years on, the troops of the Austrian Emperor Leopold I marched through Wieliczka. Although their aim was to fight the Swedes alongside the Poles, they sacked Wieliczka just like the invaders. Their assistance was paid for by King John Casimir, who borrowed money against half the income from the Cracow salt mines. Over the next two years, rebel Polish troops troubled Wieliczka. In 1702 royal troops under Stanisław Ernest Denhoff of Lithuania were quartered in the town. Due to a conflict with the town's inhabitants a pogrom ensued, which culminated in the killing of the town mayor.

Since the mine's substructure was in a shambles, a wave of cave-ins was reported. Cracks appeared in the walls of a church and castle buildings collapsed. The imposing "royal chamber" was burnt down together with the castle's second floor during one of the numerous fires. The chapel was destroyed by the Swedes, while the "town hall" had to be supported by a wooden scaffolding, its southern wall having completely gone.

Epidemics added to the tragedies. In the 1650s more than a hundred people died in Wieliczka every week. The mine ceased to operate for lack of workers. The plague returned in 1664 and in 1676—79. In the early 18th century, the inhabitants were decimated by two more epidemics of the bubonic plague. The town became deserted. In 1665 Wieliczka had fewer than 500 inhabitants, a half of what the population had been in the 14th century.

Such was the time when Sebastian's descendants accumulated their fortune. His son, Stanisław Lubomirski, started off by repeating his father's favourite trick: in the 1620s he opened his own salt mine in the village of Siercza near Wieliczka. The name of the well was "Kunegunda" and it was not long before the output of the well started aggressively to compete with royal salt.

Stanisław Lubomirski died in 1649. The well was inherited by his three sons: Konstanty, starost of Sącz, Aleksander Michał, Royal Master of the Horse, and Jerzy Sebastian, Grand Marshal of Poland. The last of these, named after his grandfather, inherited his ruthlessness and factiousness. During negotiations in 1651 he assaulted a royal official. He was saved from serious consequences by Queen Marie Louise, however, the Lubomirskis had to give the "Kunegunda" shaft to the Treasury with no compensation. Although a document to this effect was signed by the family, they did not bother to respect it. The power of the king is too weak and the Lubomirskis are too strong for anyone to force them to comply with the verdict.

In 1664 Jerzy Sebastian Lubomirski was charged with high treason. The parliamentary court *in absentia* sentenced him to exile and infamy. Lubomirski sought refuge in Silesia, where under the Holy Roman Emperor's protection, he entered into political schemes with Moscow, trying to persuade Russia to declare war on King John Casimir of Poland. In 1665 Lubomirski headed his troops during a raid on Polish territory, ostensibly to defend the "golden freedom" of the gentry. Together with rebel royal troops and noblemen who sided with him, Lubomirski sparked off a civil war. In 1666 he defeated troops loyal to the king under Stefan Czarniecki in the battle of Mątwy and forced King John Casimir to seek a truce under his terms, which was agreed upon at Łęgonice on the Pilica river. Lubomirski's rebellion foiled plans to strengthen the authority of the king and to streamline democracy in Poland.

THE LUBOMIRSKI
SAGA CONTINUED

In this way, the grandson of a petty nobleman exerted a pernicious influence on the fate of the country...

Aleksander Michał did not side with his brother during the rebellion, remaining faithful to the king. His reward was the annulment of the 1651 verdict. Shortly before his abdication in 1688, King John Casimir allowed the "Kunegunda" salt mine formally to return to the Lubomirskis. The fact was, however, that in practice the family had never respected the previous ruling.

Successive mine masters appointed by the king constantly eyed the activities of the Siercza well with suspicion since it was a considerable obstruction for their business. However, for the time being there was little they could do to curb the power of the mighty Lubomirskis. Nevertheless, they scrupulously collected arguments that might prove useful in a possible show-down, just in case. In 1670 it seemed that the time had come. Due to the mine master's intervention, the then king Michael Korybut Wiśniowiecki sent commissioners to Wieliczka to examine whether the Lubomirskis were mining salt from their own estate or whether they infringed upon the deposits within the estate owned by the king. Reports by Wieliczka management officials were confirmed. The Lubomirskis had in fact extended their galleries into the royal estate and started mining salt there. The offence was proved, but it seems that the Lubomirskis were too strong since the royal administration failed to draw conclusions from the findings of the commision.

The final act of the salt feud opened in 1714. The administration of the mines was taken over by chancellor Jan Przebendowski, but actual management was in the hands of inspector Franciszek Teodor Reyna, a confidant of King Augustus (II) the Strong. He was resolute, consistent in his views and, what irritated the master of "Kunegunda" the most, he would not accept bribes. The Lubomirskis had had their day. Conflicting interests within the family led to their gradual weakening, which meant they could no longer disregard the law with impunity. Reyna took advantage of this and decided to put an end to the century-old competition between Wieliczka and "Kunegunda."

Under a ruling of the royal commission, the well was confiscated. The actual shaft was filled up and underground galleries were included in the royal mine. This way the Lubomirskis' contacts with salt deposits near Cracow were brought to an end. Salt had been for them the source of enormous riches that had first been tapped by Sebastian 136 years earlier and which lay at the foundation of the fortune of one of the mightiest magnate families in Poland...

SAXON MANAGEMENT

The year 1697 saw the access to the Polish throne of Frederick Augustus (II) of the Wettin dynasty, an event that opened a personal union between Poland and Saxony that lasted more than half a century. For Poland, this was a period of the final decline of the state but to the Cracow mines, the Saxon rule was a godsend.

Saxony at that time had a developed economy with a strong, centralized administration. Aware of the financial rewards wise management of the salt mines might bring, King Augustus II resolutely set about streamlining the operation of the Wieliczka and Bochnia mines. Although weak royal authority restricted the scope of reforms (it was still impossible to rid Wieliczka of the burden of annuities, allowances etc.), this did not rule out work to improve the technical aspect of the mine. Extraction methods were brouht up to date and organizational changes were introduced. In this, King Augustus II relied on experts from Saxony. Since executive posts in the mines could only be filled by the Polish gentry, new positions for the Saxons were created. They became shop stewards and inspectors. Possessed of wide prerogatives, they soon took over control of the mine.

Apart from technical improvements, which we shall be returning to, their greatest achievement was to put labour organization in order. Executive pay was substantially increased. A detailed list of responsibilities for each post was drawn up and an efficient system of control was introduced. Mismanagement was severely punished. The workers' wages were arranged according to a new, simplified list. Those measures helped diffuse social tensions and enhanced work discipline. The system of material supply was improved. Until then, officials had found it easy to embezzle supplies. Strict austerity measures were also introduced.

The Saxon rule was the last period in the history of Polish mine masters, an epoch during which mine masters had demonstrated interest in activities exceeding the scope of salt mining. There were to be no more names that entered Polish history books not as mine masters alone, but as talented finance ministers and arts sponsors like the Boners. There were also to be no more shady characters like Sebastian Lubomirski. The 18th century saw the advent of the epoch of technocrats who were less colourful and versatile, seemingly lacking glamour, but whose greatness lay in their efficient work. Their greatness may not be traced in the mansions in the Cracow Market Square or in castles in Little Poland. It is to be found on the pages of studies in the fields of economics, land surveying, geology. Telling evidence of their work are the walls of the chambers and galleries of the Wieliczka mine.

In 1764 Stanisław Poniatowski, a protégé of the Empress Catherine II who dispatched Russian troops to surround Warsaw during the election, was elected to the Polish throne. Four years later saw the formation of the Confederacy of Bar, which started struggle under the slogans of Poland's sovereignty, the "Holy Catholic Faith" and noblemen's privileges. The confederacy appreciated the fact that the Cracow salt mines were a major source of income for the Treasury. Their troops seized Wieliczka and on 7 June 1768 mine officials took an oath of allegiance to the confederacy. Wieliczka received the confederates with goodwill, but it soon appeared that although the confederates were strong enough to seize the town, they could not afford to pay for its upkeep. In the 1768—71 period the mine changed hands several times. The leaders of the confederacy insisted on maintaining former production levels and trade, while Russian troops ordered excavated salt to be transported back down into the galleries, to prevent the confederates from seizing the mineral. Each of the sides requisitioned the receipts of the mine for its own purposes. The then mine master Wojciech Kluszewski proved to be a skilful diplomat trying to placate both sides.

Wojciech Kluszewski was the last Polish mine master at Wieliczka. In 1772 Poland was subjected to the first partitioning. On 10 June Austrian troops moved into the town and in late August mine management underwent a radical reorganization. The Austrians offered Kluszewski, who had been an efficient manager, the opportunities to remain on the board of the mine, but he did not accept the nomination from the invaders. The reorganization saw the disappearance of traditional posts that had originated as early as in the 14th century, during the reign of King Casimir the Great. In their place, the Higher Salt-Mining Office and the Miners' Court of the Austrian civil service subordinate to the court chamber in Vienna, were formed. Executive posts in the mine management were occupied by the Austrians, and the German

UNDER FOREIGN RULE

became the official language. All previous financial responsibilities such as annuities and allowances were annulled.

The Napoleonic era inspired hope of regaining independence by Poland. The Duchy of Warsaw was formed in 1807 due to the disintegration of the Prussian state of the Hohenzollern dynasty. However, the situation of Wieliczka did not change and the mine remained under Austrian rule. Hostilities soon flared up between Austria and France. Napoleon's victory in the battle of Wagram forced Austria to sign a peace treaty at Schönbrunn in 1809. During peace negotiations Wieliczka became one of the major bones of contention. The Duchy of Warsaw, which had no other salt deposits, was reluctant to give up Wieliczka and Austria too did not want this lucrative source of income to slip out of its hands. As a result, compromise solution was proposed: the mine was to be jointly owned by Austria and the Duchy of Warsaw ruled by King Frederick Augustus of Saxony. The two sides were jointly to cover expenses and share the profit. The joint management of Count Ksawery Wiesiołowski, the Duchy's commissioner, and Baron Anton Baum, who represented Austria, was a constant source of conflicts that paralyzed all management activities. Thus, after two years the two sides agreed to introduce a uniform Austrian management.

In 1813, after the outbreak of the Austrian-Saxon war, Austria seized Wieliczka for all of 105 years. A degree of change was introduced in the late 1860s when the Austrian monarchy made attempts to liberalize domestic relations, following a war against Prussia and in the face of unrest in Hungary. That period of the province's autonomy marked the subordination of the mine to the National Treasury Board in Lvov. The Polish language was restored as the official one and the Poles were admitted to higher executive posts.

The Austrian rule also marked changes in the sphere of organization and management. Together with Austrian officials there came a fresh wave of mining experts who intruduced innovative extraction methods. The long period of Austrian rule exerted a beneficial influence on the technical shape of the mine. It injected a necessary dose of stability which was essential following the turbulent years of devastation and looting by disorderly troops.

Construction work was in full swing on the surface. Virtual palaces appeared, built by the Konopkas, Przychockis and other families that became rich on salt trade. A public park was planted where a theatre company regularly performed for a time. The town acquired a water supply system and electricity from a power station constructed next to the mine. In 1857 a railway line was opened between Cracow and Wieliczka. Prior to that the only way to get from Wieliczka to Cracow was by stage-coach, which took all of two hours, or by express mail coach which saved three quarters of an hour. Four years

later the railway tracks were extended to the "Regis" well. The cars were initially drawn by horses and from 1891 by a steam locomotive. Old, wooden structures over shafts gradually disappeared and were replaced with brickwork. The Austrians renovated and reconstructed the Wieliczka castle. During the maintenance work, a sizeable part of ancient architectural heritage was lost. The castle preserved that shape until World War II when one of a few bombs to hit Wieliczka destroyed its oldest and most valuable part, known as the House of the Salt Mine.

The peaceful development of the town was twice broken off by epidemics of cholera and by a major fire caused by the liking of Austrian officials for Viennese bread. It was in the bakery of a Vienna baker by the name of Rappaport that fire broke out on 24 July 1877. A part of the city was destroyed in the conflagration, including houses that lined the market square, the seat of the municipal council, a chemist's and two schools.

The fact that the mine and the town developed quite rapidly could not overshadow the fact of the exploitation of Polish workers by the invaders. In 1798 the eminent Polish economist Stanisław Staszic wrote bitterly, "Down in the mine, when I walked amidst untold riches of Poland that are now in the hands of the invaders, my heart was gripped by sorrow. I felt we were wicked not to have left a sign of how we felt about the loss. If I were a king, I would either emerge victorious or I would fall at Wieliczka..."

On 1 November 1918 the people of Wieliczka tore Austrian eagles down from public buildings. On 9 November a meeting of a newly created Workers' Council decided to change the names of the mine wells. Instead "Emperor Franz Josef", "Duke Rudolph", "Empress Elisabeth", "Josef" and "Franz," Polish names "Regis", "Daniłowicz", "Kinga", "Kościuszko" and "Paderewski" appeared. After 146 years the mines near Cracow again became the supplier of salt to the independent Polish state. The situation had changed, though. The seizure of Wieliczka by Austria had prompted an intensive search for salt deposits elsewhere on the Polish territory. The development of drilling techniques facilitated the discovery of rich salt deposits in the Kuyavy region in the 1870s. Salt mines were developed in Inowrocław and at Wapno. Thus, the Cracow salt mines had ceased to be the sole source of the precious mineral in Poland.

Since then the history of the ancient mine has run a normal course. Mining methods were gradually developed, production grew steadily and the normal production rate was maintained. In 1939 another period of foreign occupation started. Apart from mining, the Germans meant to use Wieliczka as an underground arms factory. In the final stages of World War II, preparatory installations were under way. Wieliczka miners got their own back on the Germans by hiding the Jews in the mine and stealing explosives that were then used by Polish partisans who sabotaged Nazi train transports. Tunnels dug to underground food storage chambers enabled many a Polish family to survive wartime food shortages.

The ordeal of the Nazi occupation over, salt from Wieliczka returned to Polish tables.

MERCHANTS AND THE SALT BLACK MARKET

In the days of old, when salt played the role of currency, salt trade was in the hands of officials authorized by the monarch to mint coins. In the 13th century, the distribution of the mineral slipped from their hands, but the principles of separation of salt production from the salt trade was maintained. This was reaffirmed and laid down in detail by the statute passed by King Casimir the Great, which forbade the mine management to deal in the salt trade.

The mine master was authorized to sell salt only to those who were entitled to re-sell it under the royal charter. Merchants who enjoyed the exclusive right to purchase salt directly from the mines were initially recruited only from among Wieliczka, Bochnia and Cracow burghers. It was from them that merchants from other towns could buy salt *en masse,* while the inhabitants of Wieliczka, Bochnia and Cracow were able to buy salt for their daily use.

Salt trade regulations made up a fairly complicated system that enabled the monarch to control the development of towns, the saturation of the market in particular regions of the country and also the directions of exports. The king decided what kind of salt a merchant was allowed to deal in, its price and transport routes. He also issued orders or bans on sales in particular towns and decided when, where and how the retail trade should be conducted. Cracow, Wieliczka and Bochnia merchants were allowed to purchase salt blocks, the most precious form of mineral. Kazimierz and Kleparz merchants were also authorized to purchase salt by King Ladislaus Jagiello, but they were only allowed to buy fine salt, sales of which were less profitable. Differences in salt prices made it possible to win foreign markets. The statute passed by King Casimir the Great set the price of a *cetnar* of salt (about 65 kg.) to be sold at home at 12 groszys, while salt exported to Spisz and Hungary was to cost only four groszys. Orders to transport salt via particular towns protected their interests. Those towns enjoyed the right of storage, under which merchants were obliged to stop and display their goods for sale. All these measures enabled the monarch fully to control the home market and stimulate profitable exports.

In the north of Poland, Cracow salt competed with French and Spanish salt brought by sea. Particularly dynamic attempts to win this market were recorded in the 16th century when the Cracow salt mines opened their own salt storage facilities along the Vistula river (at Solec Street in Warsaw, at Zakroczym, Płock and Nieszawa), along the Narew, Bug and Wieprz rivers. The fact that salt was transported to the mines' own storage facilities was meant to make merchants in the north interested in the product and to win the favour of noblemen who could collect allowances of Lenten salt. However, it appeared in practice that transportation down the Vistula river proved to be unreliable and risky. West-bound exports of the Polish salt reached Wrocław as early as the 14th century where it successfully competed with salt mined in Halle in Saxony. In Hungary, Polish merchants had to compete with the mineral originating in Transylvania. The eastern limits of Wieliczka salt sales were in the Lublin province where Ukrainian salt was also sold.

The salt trade was a profitable occupation. The Cracow guild of salt merchants was by no means among the poorest. Down the ages, its members occupied a number of important posts in the town council (up to mayor). Customs records are telling evidence of the size of trade conducted by the merchants. In the second half of 1589, for instance, Cracow city limits were crossed by more than a thousand transports of salt bound for exports. The guild actively participated in public life, religious ceremonies, shooting events and in the defence of the city, alongside other craft guilds. It was the responsibility of the salt merchants to maintain a turret in a section of the city walls between the Wiślna Gate and St. Anne's Wicket.

Relations between mine management and salt merchants had their ups and downs. It should be noted, however, that the royal company protected its customers' interests. The management took account of the merchants' transportation capabilities. Blocks of salt meant for exports were smaller and thus

24

easier to carry along mountain roads. In the mid-17th century, plans to form small-sized blocks of salt were shelved since the capacity of merchants' waggons would not be fully used. The merchants insisted on purchasing large blocks for other reasons, too. Firstly, customs fees had to be paid irrespective of the weight of a block. Only the number of blocks mattered. Secondly, during transportation and storage larger blocks decayed to a lesser extent than smaller ones and thus losses were not as high. Recommendations issued by royal commissioners often pointed to the need to treat customers in a polite way. In 1592, for instance, mine officials were instructed to serve merchants efficiently and politely, so that customers did not have to lose time in inns.

Conflicts that developed between merchants and the mine were frequently over the price of salt. In the late 16th century, when the costs of materials used for production grew substantially, the mines tried to raise the prices of blocks of salt. The merchants protested quoting ancient privileges, in which the prices of particular kinds of salt were strictly defined. The mines reacted in a way familiar to many a contemporary producer: although the price of salt blocks was maintained, their production was substantially lowered. Several new block sizes were introduced instead of the previous uniform one. The new products differed mainly in price. Because of the lack of traditionally-sized blocks, the merchants had to buy one of the new varieties, paying higher prices.

At Wieliczka, salt was picked up from a storage facility close to a well. A bustling square was situated in front of the store, which was surrounded by stables and barns. The square was usually filled to capacity with horse-drawn waggons awaiting the loading of salt. Merchants from all over Poland could be spotted in the square, sometimes from the most remote corners of the country. The atmosphere of a merry social gathering was enhanced by the mine's hospitality. The drivers were treated to bread, cottage cheese and beer and sometimes even to hot meals, all at the expense of the mine.

The purchasing of salt at Wieliczka was not only limited to necessary formalities and payments shown in the price list. It was common knowledge that a merchant could be issued blocks mined from deposits of varying purity and that the time they spent waiting for the loading of salt onto their waggons could vary widely. This was entirely up to the mine workers, each of whom was after a bribe. In 1595 women stall keepers testified before a royal commission that those who offered gifts to the workers were issued better quality salt. Royal regulations provided for stiff penalties for workers who accepted bribes for preferential treatment of customers. Competition for pure salt sometimes assumed rather ugly forms. Records from 1597 show that a Jan Orczyński badly beat up a Zofia Kropidło, the widow of Mateusz, a Cracow salt merchant, who arrived at Wieliczka to buy salt.

Salt was loaded on waggons drawn by two to six horses. Carrying the load was by no means an easy task, since the weight of a salt block often exceeded two tonnes. Roads close to the mines and chambers along the Vistula river were repaired by the mine, but further away from Wieliczka it was rough going. Heavy waggons got stuck in mud and sand, or broke axles in pot-holes. Rain caused additional problems: the soluble load had to be carefully protected against damp. Last but not least, bands of robbers were after the precious salt. Actually, a few mine masters, notably Sebastian Lubomirski, were themselves involved in robberies and other underhand dealings.

The Vistula river was another major transport route. In spring and autumn, when the water was high, huge barges plied downriver to the mine's storage facilities in central and northern Poland. Individual merchants usually had too

small amounts of salt at their disposal to float them downriver. After all, a barge in the 18th century could carry up to six hundred barrels of salt. The floating of salt was initially organized by Cracow and Kazimierz burghers and later by Cracow, Oświęcim and Sandomierz gentry.

The only group of people free of transportation headaches were the Wieliczka inhabitants. They were allowed to sell salt at market stalls and — which was a rather exceptional privilege — in their own homes. Fulvius Ruggieri, who visited the salt mines in 1565 wrote that nearly all people who lived close to the mine stored a salt block in front of their houses and chipped as much as they needed off the block. That description was slightly exaggerated. After all, the blocks were quite expensive and to afford one, several Wieliczka burghers had to pool their resources. It seems that with the exception of a handful of wealthy salt merchants, Wieliczka burghers rather dealt in cheaper varieties of salt, either in lumps or fine salt manufactured from brine.

In Cracow, salt vendors had their stalls in the Market Square where Szczepańska Street starts. Initially, a storage facility was also situated there, where salt transported from Wieliczka was kept. It was there that wholesale trade was conducted, that is where whole salt blocks or barrels were sold. Blocks were also broken up into smaller lumps that were later sold at particular stalls. The problem was that heavy waggons that carried salt damaged flag-stones, so in the late 16th century, salt storage facilities were transferred behind the city walls next to the New Gate (now the junction with Sienna Street). The stalls remained at the Market Square and were open daily from morning till dusk. They were only closed on Mondays, church holidays, and because of other prominent events like the funeral of a member of the salt merchants' guild.

An important, though difficult or even practically impossible responsibility of the guild was to guard the monopoly on sale and distribution of salt. Complaints lodged with the town council, mine master and the king show that the merchants had to face up to a number of legal and illegal competitors in this lucrative trade. The former included recipients of annuities and allowances. Even if they did not sell the salt they collected, they had enough of it for their own needs and thus the merchants could not hope to sell them any. The same was true about the suppliers of materials that were used in production, mainly tallow and iron brought to Bochnia from Hungary and to Wieliczka from Silesia. Until the mid-16th century the salt mines paid for those products with low-grade salt.

A major blow to the interests of salt merchants was dealt by the Nieszawa statutes that allowed the gentry to collect Lenten salt. Thus not only manor houses and noblemen's estates ceased to buy salt from them, but also the farmers were forced to purchase it from their overlords. Although the privilege made it clear that Lenten salt was only designed for home use by the gentry, the low prices paid to the mine by the noblemen made re-selling Lenten salt a lucrative trade.

Another source that contributed to the saturation of the market were allowances issued to mine workers. Loose women used to spend hours waiting in front of the shafts offering their company to the miners for fewer than three kilos of salt. That was why royal commissioners forbade women to loiter near the shaft entrance. Royal regulations called for restraint in pilfering, explaining the simple economic rules governing the salt market. Those arguments did not convince the work force. Since pilfering added about two and a half tonnes of salt to the Wieliczka trade a day, regulations were issued under which the miners were obliged to sell such illicit salt to the mine.

Large quantities of stolen salt also wound up on the Wieliczka salt market. The phenomenon could be observed particularly during wars or when the mines were managed by dishonest supervisors who themselves set an example in how to earn money by cheating the Treasury. Miners carried salt under their clothes on leaving the mine. The name of a worker who was caught pilfering salt was entered in mine registers. Under regulations laid down by the king himself a worker caught red-handed was suspended for half a year. A repeated offence entailed his suspension for a year and if he was caught for the third time, he was banned for life from working in the mine. Workers who transported salt from the mine to the warehouse, weighed it and bulk-loaded it on merchants' waggons, enjoyed particularly good opportunities to pilfer salt. Drivers who carried it from the mine to the river port on the Vistula opened barrels on the way, emptied them and filled them with mud or stones (for which they could have their waggon together with horses confiscated). In a word — everyone involved in salt production and trade stole as much as he could, if only offered a chance to. Royal instructions were regularly amended to prevent pilfering. They listed all kinds of regulations to forestall all possibilities of underhand dealings. An instruction, for instance, stated that a scale used to weigh salt should be maintained by a locksmith and injected with oil every four months so that its readings were accurate.

A salt guard subordinated to the Cracow chamberlain until the 17th century and then under the control of the mine management, was responsible for prosecuting illicit trade. Its members confiscated all consignments that were not accompanied by a consignment note issued by the mine management.

The epoch of the salt merchants ended when Poland lost her independence. In 1772, when Wieliczka was seized by the Austrians, all previous privileges were annulled. In the Duchy of Warsaw people representing all social groups were allowed to engage in the salt trade over the entire Polish territory, to establish warehouses and to earn profits from salt sales.

Technology

On their way to work they pass by a small, single-storey building of the Museum. Twenty years ago as excavating for its foundations began, remnants of a mediaeval salt-works were unearthed. They go into the cages of the mine lift in the "Kinga" shaft named after the queen who, according to legend, miraculously brought the salt wealth from Hungary to Poland. A hundred and seventy metres underground they are welcomed — just as 300 years ago — by horses' whinnying that echoes in the underground stable. They board the metal cars of the electric railway. In the narrow cracks of the small windows the gallery's walls begin to stream past. The now half-effaced, tooth-shaped traces of the wedges with which their predecessors split off huge blocks of salt several centuries ago are flashing by. Then begin corridors with the characteristic set-offs left behind by cutting machines in the early 20th century. After a four kilometre ride they get off in a semi-circular gallery traced by regular arches of the modern lining. They follow the inclined drifts to where, beyond the blind wall, lurks the past of the mine...

Wieliczka miners' daily lesson in history: seven hundred years of human thought and toil encased in three hundred kilometres of underground chambers and galleries.

FROM A SALT-WORKS
TO A... SALT-WORKS

Our forefathers took an interest in salt about 7,000 years ago, in the initial phase of the Neolithic age. This was related to the development of agriculture and the attendant change in their diet: plant products, unlike animal meat, no longer ensured the organism the required quantity of that compound. It began to be produced by evaporating brine scooped from salty springs.

The first traces of salt-panning in the environs of Cracow come from the middle of the Neolithic age (3500—2500 years B.C.) and are related to the population of the Lengyel culture. Excavations indicate that apart from the primitive ways of evaporating small quantities of brine for individual needs there had existed, even then, methods of "industrial production" aimed at a salt surplus intended for barter. The technology was not too complicated: salty water from a spring flowed down clay-inlaid grooves dug in the ground and into square-shaped pits. Thence the brine was scooped into broad earthenware vessels which were placed over a fire. The dense salt mass obtained by partial evaporation of water was put into peak-bottomed mugs and dried by being placed in glowing embers. That produced conic salt cakes weighing between 0.7 and 1 kg., which served as coins in those times. Salt as a currency is used, in fact, as late as the beginning of the 13th century, which may attest to its exceptional importance in economic life. Subsequent salt-panning settlements, unearthed by Wieliczka archaeologists, belong to the Lusatian culture and come from the Hallstatt period (700—400 years B.C.). No major changes had occurred in the mode of production except that for the final moulding of the salt cakes — just like elsewhere in contemporary Europe — special cups were used. Salt lumps were cylinder-like and weighed about 0.5 kg.

The further improvements of the installations are linked with the period of Roman influence and with the population of what is known as the Tyniec mixed culture group, which inhabited the environs of Cracow from the 1st century B.C. to the middle of the 1st century A.D. The brine grooves and the earth receptacles were now wood-lined; the entire installations were protected from precipitations with roofing and lids. The greatest technological achievement of that period, however, was the use of sedimentation basins; before the brine reached the receptacle from the spring it flowed through two basins in which mechanical impurities were deposited. This procedure helped improve the quality of the end product — the salt cakes were now much purer.

The salt-panning technology proved to be exceptionally resistent to all sorts of innovation. From the Neolithic age right down to the Middle Ages production took the same form: the raw material came from natural surface springs, the brine was collected in receptacles doubling as sedimentation basins, and the salt-panners' efforts produced salt cakes of standard weight and shape. The evaporation itself consisted of two stages (concentrating of the salt mass in big vessels and baking in smaller ones) and proceeded over open hearths. Only the Middle Ages brought changes in the way of obtaining raw material (brine wells, mine waters, fine rock salt dissolved in fresh water), in the methods of production (single-stage evaporation in metal pans) as well as in the appearance of the final product (boiled salt instead of salt cakes).

Before we deal with that mediaeval revolution in Polish salt-making, however, it should be added that the natural brine springs continued in use for long centuries. Aleksander Heiter von Schonweth, who on behalf of Austria after the first partition of Poland, took over the administration of the Cracow salt mines, said in a 1775 report that the people of Rabka used brine from the local springs for salting meals, bread-baking and cattle-watering. A similar situation prevailed at the time in the village of Sól near Żywiec. Since this was hurting the interests of the state monopoly, the Austrian government ordered the wells encased and closed. Protocols have been preserved in the Archives of the Cracow Salt Mines Museum showing that Austrian officials made periodic inspections of the closed springs.

Let us get back to the Middle Ages, though. In the 10th century the Polish state emerged and the family-tribal system turned into a feudal society. Salt-making became one of the royal privileges and was from then on to constitute an important element of the prince's economic power.

In the mid-11th century earthenware pots and open hearths disappeared from the Wieliczka salt-works. Brine was now made in flat, rectangular, shallow metal vessels set in a stone foundation. The vessels soon reached relatively large dimensions — by archaeologists' reckoning the pans held some 1400 litres of brine in the mid-12th century.

The most important development, however — one that was decisive in the history of Polish salt — was the gradual exhaustion of the surface springs around Wieliczka and Bochnia. The greater efficiency of the equipment and the growing demand for salt forced the salt-makers to deepen their wells and then — at the turn of the 11th and 12th centuries — to sink wells in search of underground brine lodes. This, of course, was related both to the new skill of lining to keep the wells from collapsing, and to the putting in of hoisting gear. It may well be that it was during the deepening of one such well that surprised salt-makers had their first glimpse of a hard, greenish lump of rock salt...

At the turn of the 11th and 12th centuries at least 12 salt-making centres were active in the environs of Cracow, the major ones being Wieliczka, Bochnia and Sidzina. Their output not only met the needs of the inhabitants of Cracow and district but also allowed for some export. In the Polish lands only Rus and Pomerania (thanks to the brine-spring in Kołobrzeg) were self-sufficient; Mazovia and Great Poland — despite the existence of a few small salt-works in their territory — had to import salt. It was Silesia that nature had skimped most in saline springs — the needs of its population had to be met with imports from Saxony and even from Hungary. It was not until rock-salt deposits started to be mined that these problems were solved — for southern Poland at any rate.

In 1251 the first shaft at Bochnia became operational and a few years later one at Wieliczka. From that time right down to the beginning of the 20th century salt-panning became a minor activity of the Cracow mines, treated almost as utilization of "production waste". A "*karbaria*" (which is what a salt-panning works was called) would receive less attention from the royal administration and it would be leased more often than a mine. This may account for the fact that while in the West production methods were gradually being perfected, little changed in the Cracow salt-works.

The raw material was supplied by waters penetrating the underground pits and dissolving the salt deposit. The brine thus produced was brought up and channelled in wooden ducts to timber-lined receptacles. In the 16th century these earth basins were replaced by tanks placed on special scaffolding. Supplies of brine, however, were erratic, the man in charge being guided more by the mine's safety than the salt-works' needs. Also the degree of salt concentration varied, all depending both on the route that the waters had

covered down in the mine and on their contact with the deposit. That is why relatively early on, the rum — fine, impure salt obtained during tunnelling of galleries and furnaces and preparing chambers for operation — began to be utilized. The rum excavated in the mine was loaded into baskets and dipped in tanks with unsaturated brine or fresh water from nearby streams; the salt dissolved in the water and the rock impurities remained in the basket. From the tank the brine ran into the pan. The salt thus obtained was shovelled out and — after final drying — loaded into barrels. The process of evaporating one portion took four hours in the mid-16th century. "At Wieliczka every four hours boiled salt is heaped into pyramids on plaited mats," wrote Jodok Willich, the Warmia scholar who visited the Cracow salt mines in 1543. During Willich's time a single portion of brine yielded close on 300 kg. of salt and two hundred years later even over 1100 kg. The entire installations were housed in a wooden shed called a tower (the name came probably from as early as the times of brine wells when the salt-panning works building had to have a tall, pointed roof to accommodate the crane inside it). Several such towers (in the early 16th century there were six of them at Wieliczka) made up an enterprise called a "*karbaria*". Work organization and production technology in particular towers were in the charge of the salt-makers; there were two of them at all times; they took 12-hour turns since the salt-panning works operated non-stop. Special workers saw that the brine had the proper concentration, removed the impurities gathering on the surface of the solution and shovelled out the salt after evaporation.

With time, many of those functions became titular dignities: the king would confer them on his courtiers or on people who had served the state well, because of the attendant benefits, and these beneficiaries would hire specialists to do the work for them. In 1503 the privilege of taking the sold salt out of the storehouse was conferred on the royal courtier Jan Guth for life; the function of controller of the outgoing carts and that of guard went in 1509 to the Lvov canon Mikołaj de Cazanow. The dignity of Wieliczka salt-panning master was held by the eminent humanist, historian and secretary to King Sigismund I, Jost Ludwik Decjusz (Decius), and from 1567 for life by Decjusz's son, Ludwik.

It would seem that after averting the "raw-material crisis" caused by the exhaustion of the surface brine springs towards the end of the 13th century, nothing could now threaten the Cracow salt-works. Brine was ample even when mine waters were not "brought up" into the world (this custom — a threat to the security of the headings — took hold in the second half of the 16th century; the waters were gathered in worked-out chambers); the salt-works then utilized the rum that was now dissolved after being brought up to the surface. Now, during the 16th century the salt-works began visibly to decline; while at the beginning of the century boiled salt accounted for some 37% of Wieliczka's total production, towards the end of the century for as little as about 5%. That was due to "energy" problems: the lack of wood. The salt-works needed a lot of it: the evaporation of a single brine portion in a pan ate up a whole cartload of fuel; in 1527 the Wieliczka hearths used up more than 11,500 such cartloads, while enormous quantities of wood also — indeed, primarily — had to go to the mine: without huge chocks and thick shores the roofs of the underground chambers would collapse.

In 1564 the royal commissioners gave the alarm: "The woods have gone and this salt-panning works is going to go, too... It would have been gone by now had His Royal Majesty not deigned to make available the forest about which Mr Żupnik [the salt-mine master] says that it is going to give out already this year." In the following year the king decreed that boiled salt be sold exclusively to those carters bringing with them the required quantity of fuel but the royal decree could not have improved the situation since it was repealed before long. The salt-makers adopted a number of conservation measures; they saw to it, for instance, that without good reason the fires should not be put out under the pans since to re-warm them took large quantities of fuel. In the 1649 instructions to Jan Weihardt of Wrzeszczowice, of whom we have already heard, who was taking over the salt-works, the king obliged the deputy salt-works master to see to it that the water in the pans be properly salinated or else large quantities of wood were used up to little avail.

Towards the end of the 16th century, attempts were made to deal with the awkward situation in another way: salt-panning works appear in Silesia, in central and northern Poland in parts abounding in forests. They bring over from Wieliczka barrels with salt rum and dissolve it in fresh water on the spot. One of them — in Dobiegniew in Kuyavy — is a branch of the Wieliczka salt-panning works and belongs to the king. The others are set up by private companies under special charters. It should be noted that even granting such a charter, the king does not neglect his salt monopoly: he makes the reservation that at the end of a stipulated period of time (2—15 years) the salt-works becomes royal property.

The first privately-owned salt-works was set up by brothers Stefan and Jan Loiss in Toruń in the early 1570s. In 1577 King Stephen Báthory allowed the Loiss to sink — at their own cost — a special shaft at Wieliczka to supply raw material to the newly established salt-works. The Cracow one was at the time held on lease by Prospero Provana, a man who looked after his own interests much better than the king's. In the same year Provana set up his private salt-works in Stężyca on the Wieprz. A year later he became a shareholder of the Bydgoszcz salt-works which he equipped, *nota bene*, with the installations of the royal towers he had shut down at Wieliczka. No wonder then that Provana was not interested to see the Loiss shaft develop successfully; help could be expected either from his successor at the post of salt-mine master, the notorious Sebastian Lubomirski (the latter bought the Bydgoszcz salt-works from Provana in 1583). The Toruń company, in turn, did nothing to protect the headings, and went for the most raw material at the least cost. Moreover, the division of competences between this salt-works and the Toruń salt-makers is not particularly clear: the shaft was the property of the Loiss, the extraction of rum was also their business but the salt mine was supposed to work those sections of the deposit from which salt could be obtained in the shape of blocks.

All that gave rise to continual quarrels: the company complained that Provana made it hard to take rum out of Wieliczka and Lubomirski maintained that the Loiss brothers traded in rum salt, wrecked the mine and bought up material.

It may well be that the experiences with the Loiss shaft were responsible for the fact that none of the other salt-making companies was given the right to sink their own shaft, and that they simply bought the raw material from the Cracow salt mines. Apart from those already mentioned, in the last quarter of the 16th century salt-works operated — on salt rum brought over from Wieliczka — at Kodeń in Lithuania, Brześć on the Bug, Lubartów, Kozielec, Goniądz on the Biebrza, Będzin and Czajowice, as well as in Silesia: in Tarnowskie Góry and around Pszczyna. The royal administration was undoubtedly anxious to see salt-making expand in other parts of the country: this is borne out by, for example, the 1578 charter granted the Cracow voivode Piotr Zborowski which gave him very favourable terms for setting up such enterprises. Zborowski did not manage to use the opportunities he had been created (he died three years after being granted the charter) and the lot of the remaining private salt-works was not much of an inducement. Only a few of them managed to survive to the end of the 16th century but these, too, declined in the early years of the following century, one contributory factor having certainly been the difficulties involved in the transport of considerable quantities of salt rum over long distances.

During the 17th century the Wieliczka salt-works hardly existed at all. At the beginning of the following century the new administration tried to help out, which is probably related to the campaign — mounted by Augustus II — of putting things in order in the Cracow salt mines and draining the underground headings. A salt-making tower was put up in which the transport of brine to the pan was almost wholly mechanized. But these measures failed to save the salt-works: in 1724 the last salt-making tower in Wieliczka was closed down mainly owing to the lack of fuel. From that time on for nearly 200 years the Cracow salt mines did not produce panned salt. The salt rum was used to fill in the worked-out chambers, and the mine waters after being brought up onto the surface were channelled off to streams.

During those 200 years that salt-making was suspended, attempts were made, nevertheless, to return to this technology. In 1783 the administrator of the salt mines, Lichtenfels, even drew up designs for re-starting the salt-pans but they failed to gain the acceptance of the Austrian government. Thirty years later during the short period when the mine was run jointly by Austria and the Duchy of Warsaw (1809—13) the salt-works came close to being re-started. It was to be fired not with wood but with coal to be brought over from Jaworzno. (The idea of coal-firing had been put forward as early as 1631 when the royal commissioners had ordered the master of the salt mine to negotiate for coal to be brought over from Żywiec. The absence of any traces whatsoever in later documents proves that that conception was not implemented.) In 1813 even the salt-works building known as "Turówka" was put up. On 16 August 1813, Saxony declared war on Austria — the latter took over the Wieliczka salt mines as its exclusive property and the plans for coal imports from Jaworzno were abandoned. The possibility of returning to wood-firing or using coke was considered, but proved unrealistic. In a 1817 decree the Vienna parliament proclaimed that "the idea of using Wieliczka brine for salt-evaporation therefrom has to be given up once and for all". One memento of the whole business is the still-existant "Turówka" building and that "once and for all" of the Vienna parliament in this case stood for... less than 100 years.

In the years 1910—13 a modern fully-mechanized vacuum salt-works was set up. Also the method of obtaining brine was new: inside the mine what are known as "lixiviation towers" (the first one of these was put up in 1911 in the "Geisruck" chamber) were installed. These were wooden cases — from five to fifty metres high — which were filled with fine salt mined mechanically or using explosives. Through the towers ran water piped from the surface, which washed the salt and collected — now as fully-saturated brine — in tanks from which it was pumped to the salt-works.

From that time on, salt-making began quickly to regain lost ground. In 1935 the method of direct deposit — used to this day — was tried for the first time. This is the lixiviation method in which water is led in through drilled holes directly into the salt deposit (without the latter being premined) and brought up to the surface on saturation. In this way, man, who for long centuries had combatted water inundating the headings learnt to use it and today is himself letting it underground...

In 1938 rock salt was still accounting for two-thirds of the total output of Wieliczka. The final victory of salt-panning came in 1964. History had come full circle: today, just as seven centuries ago, exclusively panned salt is being manufactured...

QUEEN KINGA'S RING

It is only fitting that the story about the first shaft and the first lump of rock salt to be excavated in Polish lands should start with Queen Kinga. Such a beginning is exceedingly beneficial for any author since while scientists are still unsure where, when and in what circumstances the first mine came into being, legend entertains no (or perhaps with a single exception) doubts: salt was miraculously brought from Hungary to Poland by the Blessed Kinga...

Kinga was the daughter of the Hungarian king Béla IV and the Greek emperor's daughter Maria. In 1239 she came to Poland and here in Wojnicz she became engaged — or rather was made to become engaged — to Boleslaus, the son of the Cracow prince Leszek the White. Her fiancé was thirteen years old and Kinga five... The wedding had to wait for Kinga to come of age, i.e. turn twelve. Now, after the engagement the Hungarian princess stayed in the Cracow court to learn something of the customs of a country over which she was one day to reign. Although after barely two years she had to leave Cracow, and fairly quickly, too, she was back in 1243 after the Tartar invasion had passed by and the country's political situation cleared up. She left Poland only one more time on a short trip to Hungary to see her father. Historians suppose that she went there in search of protection against the importunities of Little Poland squires (led by the Cracow bishop Prandota) who, concerned with the fate of the dynasty, pleaded with her to break the chastity vows she had taken in her childhood. Kinga kept her vows, though, in which she was undoubtedly helped by an understanding consort: Boleslaus died on 7 December 1279 reputed "not to have known a woman", and Kinga confided in the nuns: "Of my husband I have never seen anything other than his hands and his face." After her husband's death Kinga settled in the Poor Clares Convent she had founded at Sącz and soon made it into a cultural centre influencing the whole of the country (some researchers see the Sącz convent as the birthplace of the oldest Polish song *Bogurodzica* — God's Mother). Their exceptional convergence of views on the institution of marriage produced for Kinga a beatification in 1690, and for Boleslaus the sobriquet of the Chaste that history gave him, and for the country — the extinction of the Little Poland Piast line.

33

No wonder, then, that such a saintly life made Kinga the heroine of untold myths, legends and stories. As she was coming into this world she is said to have saluted the Holy Virgin with the words: "Welcome, o Queen of the Heavens"; in infancy she did not take food on fasting days and as a small child she gave her clothes away to the poor. Poland is alleged to owe to her some of its geographical features: during a flight from Cracow in 1241 she stopped the pursuing Tartars by throwing behind her a belt and a rosary: the belt turned into the river Dunajec and the rosary into the Pieniny Mountain range. And the story about the salt goes like this:

When the Polish envoys arrived in Hungary to pick up Kinga, the young princess enquired in detail what was missing in their country. On hearing about the shortage of salt she asked her father to give her as dowry not gems and expensive robes but one of the well-known mines in Maramarosz. Béla IV could not refuse his daughter anything. So Kinga went to Maramarosz and flung her engagement ring into the adit. After arriving in Poland and a lavish wedding party, the young lady and her entire court made a trip outside Cracow. What route did she follow? Here legend behaves just as do dead-serious scientists: some maintain that the royal entourage stopped over in Wieliczka, and the others that the highway led Kinga straight to Bochnia. What all are agreed about is that from the spot Kinga had indicated in the ground a splendid lump of rock salt with her engagement ring inside was brought up...

Another version of the legend says that after she had flung her ring into the Maramarosz adit Kinga went to bed with the express order that she was not to be awakened. Before long, however, a terrible pealing rang out underground. The frightened courtiers' nerves gave out and, in spite of the orders to the contrary, they woke up the princess; had they let her have a good sleep, the salt would have got right up to the Wawel Castle and not have stopped a few kilometres short of Cracow...

The cult of the Blessed Kinga appeared among the miners of Wieliczka and Bochnia at the very beginning of the mines and is with them to this day. Already the mediaeval description of the miracles worked in the 14th century *Vita et miracula sanctae Kyngae Ducissae Cracoviensis* mentions pilgrimages from those localities to her grave in Stary Sącz; later on, mass pilgrimages from Wieliczka and Bochnia became an annual custom. During the disastrous fire at the Wieliczka mine in 1644 "all the miners and burghers led by the then administrator Adam Kazanowski, HM court marshal, made a procession to the Saint' grave in Stary Sącz, and on their return, strangely, the uncontrollable fire had been put out," wrote Feliks Boczkowski in the 19th century.

The Cracow-area miners adopted Kinga as their special patroness. The belief in the care and assistance of this saint lives on in the mine to this day. Urszula Janicka-Krzywda quotes in her work about the Wieliczka miners' beliefs, fragments of tape-recordings she made a few years ago with older miners:

"There was a cave-in down the mine and several miners had been cut off by that cave-in. Assistance was on its way to them but things were very difficult and the German engineer did not authorize new expenses for a rescue operation and maintained that those buried were sure to be dead. Then the miners went to the church to pray for those buried. According to what they said later on it was precisely during that prayer that those buried saw St. Ku-negunda [Kinga] and she led them through that cave-in into the gallery. They then reached the shaft all by themselves."

34

"There was a miner who was especially keen on Kinga because thanks to her his child had recovered from an illness. From that time on he kept praying to Kinga. Once, as he was about to go out to work in the morning he heard a voice: 'You are to take a light to the church right away.' The miner worried he'd be late for work and be punished for it but after a moment's hesitation he decided to comply with the saint's order. He took two glasses of butter and a wick and took them to the church. No sooner had he lit them under St. Kinga's picture than he heard the mine siren wail. He ran out of the church and learnt from the people that where he was supposed to have been working there had been a gas explosion."

It is time, however, to return to the beginnings of salt-making in Poland. The historians have naturally rejected the story about the miraculous transfer of the salty mineral from Hungary to Poland. The first to try — as early as the mid-16th century — to give a scientific explanation of the discovery of the salt was the earlier-mentioned Adam Schroeter. In his poem he may quote the legend but he hastens to add that this was created by "the credulous miner". According to Schroeter during Kinga's reign settlers arrived near Cracow who had seen salt mines in other countries and knew methods of prospecting for this mineral in the earth's depths.

The legend about Queen Kinga's ring, however, gave historians a lot to think about. In the Maramarosz area in Hungary salt was indeed mined — as early as in Roman times at that (if by the open-cast method). With Boleslaus the Chaste's close links with Hungary known, it seemed fairly likely that he brought over specialists to Poland and told them to prospect for salt deposits, a fact which legend immortalized in its own particular way. Even the ring motif was not dismissed; it was being defended in the 19th century by the eminent Polish historian Karol Szajnocha. According to him, Kinga might really have flung her ring into the Maramarosz adit thus symbolically taking possession of it. The ring was found by miners there who — brought later on to Poland by Boleslaus — returned it to the queen together with the first lump of salt from the Bochnia deposit they had themselves discovered.

Detailed studies of 13th century Polish-Hungarian relations had, however, failed to yield any traces to attest to the participation of Hungarians in the discovery of rock salt near Cracow. And so further searches had to be made...

The oldest Polish documents for the most part retell the legend about Kinga's miraculous importation of salt. The first one to come up with a different version of the event is the 16th-century chronicler, Marcin Bielski: "Salt found in Poland. Anno domini 1251. Salt has been found in the village of Bochnia, five miles from Cracow. It was found by peasants digging a well in the ground." The date and place are confirmed by the *Rocznik kapitulny krakowski* ("*1251 sal durum in Bochna est repertum, quod nunqua ante fuit*") and by several other documents. An interesting piece of information was contributed by Jan of Trzciana (Arundensis) who in his *Żywot błogosławionego Michała Gedroycia* writes that at Bochnia "salt has been accidentally found down a shoemaker's well". All the signs are that the beginning of salt mining really involved a certain shoemaker — the two oldest shafts of the Bochnia mine bear the names: "Gazaris" (or "Tower", and thus sited in the salt-works' compound) and "Sutoris" (or precisely "Shoemaker's"; it exists to this day and serves as a ventilation shaft).

It would seem that the above findings make it possible to pinpoint at least the date (1251) and place (Bochnia) of the discovery of salt. Historians,

35

however, dislike things that are simple and fully explained. They first set about the date: they had taken note of a document issued by Boleslaus the Chaste in 1249. In it, the prince conferred mining privileges (or the right to prospect for and exploit — on his behalf — all manner of mineral) on the Cistercian Congregation of Wąchock. The choice of the Cistercians was not accidental; the Wąchock monastery was subordinated to the abbey of Morimund in France, which at the time concerned itself with, among other things, exploitation of salt. The Cistercians (and particularly the order's convert friars who were bound by an exceptionally harsh rule to continuous and hard work) were specialists in the field of technology and industry in the Middle Ages. Some scholars link the Wąchock monastery with the beginnings of lead-ore mining around Kielce and with iron-smelting near Starachowice. In the document in question Boleslaus obliged the Cistercians to carry out what he described as "*reparatio inventii salis*". That "mending of salt equipment" did not concern — as scientists maintain — exclusively the salt-works. The overhaul of the not-too-sophisticated equipment of a salt-works would not have been beyond local salt-makers. In the following year, i.e. in 1250, Boleslaus allotted Bochnia salt to the Cracow bishop Prandota, leaving him the choice of one of the three forms of the donation: in kind, in money or "*ad formam maioris salis*", i.e. in the form of "greater salt". This is probably the first mention of rock-salt mining in Poland.

What, then, would the beginning of mining at Bochnia have been like? Jerzy Grzesiowski and Józef Piotrowicz from the Cracow Salt Mines Museum have framed the following hypothesis: the first half of the 13th century saw the accidental discovery at Bochnia — during the sinking of a brine pit — of a rock-salt deposit. Regular exploitation, however, was not started on, the salt-makers being unable to line this first shaft. The well collapsed. The chroniclers did not register the output of small quantities of "greater salt" since it was of no economic consequence. The wise Boleslaus, however, did not make light of the discovery and brought over specialists from the Cistercian order who restored the collapsed shaft and started exploitation. As for the chroniclers, they registered under the 1251 date not the discovery of a deposit but — as we would put it today — the completion of preparatory work and the beginning of industrial-scale mining.

So far the historians' deliberations had concerned solely the time of the discovery of rock salt; the place of the first mining works seemed indisputable, all the available sources indicating that mining at Wieliczka had not started until the 1280s. This seemed to be the case right down to the year 1968. This time, however, it was not historians but archaeologists who spoke. In the courtyard of the Wieliczka salt-mine castle they came on a rectangular 3.4×2.4 m. "pit" lined with not very tightly-fitting beams, connected "log-wise". In the corners of this structure there hung three thick bast ropes. Studies of the mysterious find have so far been possible down to a depth of seven metres. Scientists date it to the first half of the 13th century. The mine's oldest documents and maps do not register any shaft here but chronicles from the 1840s say that during the tunnelling of a gallery at the mine level one unknown — and unmarked on maps — heading was unearthed under the salt-mine castle. Today, those 19th century galleries being no longer accessible, it is hard to decide whether the chambers discovered then are in any way related to the find in the castle courtyard. Was it the first mining shaft whose working was interrupted by the Tartar invasions? Or was it just a prospecting shaft which, having failed to reach a deposit, had been covered in? Or, perhaps, was it an ordinary brine pit or simply a fresh-water well?

36

All these hypotheses have their fervent advocates and fierce opponents, but the final verdict can be given only by archaeological studies to be made both from the surface and from the first mine level. As things are, the cautious scientists are not stripping Bochnia of its priority and assume that it was there in the mid-13th century that rock-salt mining was started, something that Wieliczka did not copy until the 1280s. For the history of salt mining, those twenty or thirty years' difference is inconsequential, the two centres having for centuries constituted a single enterprise: the Cracow royal salt mines; but among the respective lovers of the two townlets the matter of the role that theirs has played in history used to arouse a lot of emotions. These peaked in the 19th century. While some maintained that Kinga's royal entourage stopped over in their area, the others referred to ancient authors and, using tortuous historic-cum-linguistic-cum-logical circumbendibuses, proves that salt from their area had been served on Roman tables. While the former referred to Greece the others went back to the Phoenicians! These otherwise amusing quarrels do nothing, however, to change the fact that Bochnia had all along been doomed to lose. Its fate had been decided by nature itself, and several million years ago to boot.

Twenty million years ago, in the Miocene, the Carpathian mountain chain was being formed. After the penultimate orogenic phase at the new chain's northern end where the edge of the Carpathian flysch had thrust over the earlier Mesozoic formations, a sink hole was created into which the waters of the Tethys ocean rushed. Today's Carpathian salt deposits are one result of the evaporation of waters from that sink hole. Before the final phase of the Carpathian upheaval these formed a thin layer, a belt 7—12 km. wide. The northern section of that belt lay on Mesozoic rocks, and the southern on the Carpathian flysch. The final act of orogenesis took place in two stages. First, the Carpathian flysch formations folded under the pressure from the south and the peaks of those folds "turned over" in a northern direction. The whole formation subsequently overlapped with the Mesozoic plate and with the northern portion of the salt belt covering it. A wide but thin layer of salt was thus shovelled by the powerful bulldozer of the incipient mountains into an area about a kilometre wide. The area's base was made up of Mesozoic rocks; on these lay the salt layer left intact by the tectonic movements (the northern

part of the Miocene-sea sediments); higher up were the north-pointing "up-turned" folds of the Carpathian flysch together with the remaining portion of the salt sediments. All this geological layer cake was later covered — in the Quaternary — by clays and loams.

It is worth adding that the last stage of the Carpathian upheaval has not ended yet and orogenic movements are continuing. Their action is contributing also (apart from the pressure of the overlying strata on the empty excavations) to the compression of the mine's chambers and galleries. In the Bochnia area this rock-mass pressure to the north is much more remarkable than at Wieliczka.

Under the impact of those tectonic processes the Carpathian salt deposits have adopted the shape of a few oblique scales (remnants of the "tumbled folds") sloping towards the north. At Bochnia the deposit occurs just under the ground but runs more vertically (the "scales" being positioned at an angle of 70—75 degrees). At Wieliczka the salt deposit occurs at a greater depth but it slopes more gently. However, the chief difference, which has let the Wieliczka mine last out for long centuries in an unchanged shape, consists in the fact that over the deposit, the thin layer of soft loams hold loose salt blocks of a volume from a few to 100,000 cu. m. Their origin continues to be a riddle for geologists to this day. At what moment of the complex tectonic processes did they separate from the bed? Why does the green salt they are made of differ slightly in properties (it is harder and more resistant to the overlying strata's pressure) from the grades met with in a "normal" deposit? These questions are hard to answer since a similar phenomenon is yet to be encountered anywhere in the world.

Bochnia with its typical Miocene salt deposit has shared the lot of a great many other mines. The long and high but very narrow chambers that were left after the extraction of thin (up to 12 m. thick) vertical salt layers could not resist the overlying strata's pressure for long. Bochnia salt mine's old splendour is today attested to mainly by documents; underground, only few old headings have been preserved, while the magnificent Wieliczka chambers hewn in green salt blocks still "float" in the soft loams around them.

The differences in the geological structure determined the defeat of Bochnia in its historical rivalry with Wieliczka. It had started out better placed: the salt here was found earlier on; also the town was sited earlier. Its position in relation to trade routes was also advantageous; Bochnia even stood a chance of monopolizing the whole of the trade with Hungary at the time. Casimir the Great wishing to open for the local merchants a cheap water route to the north, began some obscure project to make the Raba river navigable so as to link Bochnia with the Vistula route. The town expanded very fast; in the mid-14th century it had 2,500 inhabitants (while Wieliczka had a mere thousand).

Before long, however, the implacable verdict of nature announced itself: at Bochnia "the new miners have already found that the salt radius is very narrow ... and God knows how far down it goes". The differences in the respective extracting conditions in the two mines began to be noticeable even to visitors. Joachim Vadian in an account from the beginning of the 16th century wrote: "Down the Wieliczka mines all is sightly to the eye because even to those fearful and unaccustomed, the descent underground presents no danger to speak of, and the radiating galleries are so spacious you can walk erect. At Bochnia all the entrances run downwards and the inclined galleries make walking especially dangerous, particularly so to those unaccustomed. The ladders hanging from the shafts' walls are fixed to the oaken lining with

38

thin irons and ropes, rested on shoddy beams and are much worn by the great number of workers... I, for one, although not infrequently scared while in no small danger on land and the sea, had never thought about death more and in a more evident manner than when, led by the desire to learn of nature's riches, I had descended into that Bochnia abyss; I still recollect it like that and despite the joy of having safely watched everything, I would not like to watch it again on any occasion whatsoever... At Wieliczka things proceed at a lesser expense of labour, at Bochnia the toil involved in hoisting is enormous both because it is done in a number of places and because the hauling is done along galleries from perhaps very deep excavations. It can so happen that it [a salt block — M.H.] is hoisted with machinery made underground until — having been rolled through the chambers by all sorts of winding roads in different directions and at least six times lifted on to a higher level by those underground machines — it finally gets to the mouth of the uppermost exit shaft and is thence taken up onto the surface." Accounts from those times indicate that in the early 16th century, salt at Bochnia was brought up from a depth of more than 170 m. Concurrently, at Wieliczka exploitation was only beginning below 60 m. (in 1520 the first internal foreshaft, running from the first level downwards, was sunk). That, naturally, caused considerable hauling problems which in turn affected the price: at Wieliczka a *cetnar* (about 65 kg.) of salt cost 8 groszys and at Bochnia — 10 groszys.

Wieliczka had throughout exploited huge blocks of green salt. It was not until the early 17th century that less easily exploited deposits were started on. For the time being it was much better off: the salt here occurred relatively shallowly (starting from several metres to a few dozen metres under the surface) and in large quantities. The largest chamber of that period, the "Kloski", was 160 m. high, 40 m. wide and 96 m. long. Salt was extracted from it for more than 200 years. Extraction at the first mine level was not interrupted until the mid-18th century, more because of the danger of surface cave-ins than because of the resources running low. Bochnia had from the very beginning been doomed to a thin bed which made it impossible to hew out the most sought after salt blocks. That had an effect on the assortment: towards the end of the 17th century 80% of the Bochnia output was made up of the cheaper barrel salt (at Wieliczka — 20%). In the 15th century the respective combined volumes of output in the two centres was still about equal; in the early 16th century, 40%, and towards the end of the century a bare 20% of the salt in the market came from Bochnia.

The laws of nature are implacable. In 1565 Fulvius Ruggieri wrote about Bochnia, which after all had been the first: "The other salt mine, called Bochnia, five miles from Cracow, but by far smaller, discovered in 1251, is almost deserted by now. They say... that something like the barking of dogs, the crowing of cocks and voices of other animals can be heard down there..."

Until recently the first shaft at Wieliczka (leaving out of account the doubtful structure found at the salt-mine castle) has been known only by the name mentioned in old documents, and from 17th-century mine maps. It is known that it was called "Goryszowski" and its exit was around today's entrance to the car park in Dembowskiego Street. Since the area is built-up today, open-cast archaeological works are ruled out, and the underground headings in the "Goryszowski" shaft area have long managed to collapse. The only way out for the archaeologists was to undertake difficult mining works consisting in tunnelling through the collapsed chambers of the first mine level towards

THE OPENING OF MOUNTAINS

where, according to the old charts, the shaft should be located. Such attempts were begun in the late 1970s. In 1982 the investigation gallery came upon wooden beams 25—40 cm. in diameter joined "log-wise" and embedded in compact loams. They made up the lining of a 2×1.80 m. rectangular shaft built by Wieliczka miners exactly seven hundred years ago.

The beginnings of Polish salt mining were rather difficult. The sinkers of the first shafts had to devise their own techniques. Given the specific geological structure of the deposit in the Wieliczka and Bochnia areas they could not use the experiences of the Transylvanian centres or of Polish ore mining. The Transylvanian salt deposits were shallower; also the shafts were shorter (up to dozen or so metres) as were the headings in contemporary metal-ores mines. For the most part these were sited in a water-logged area; with the water level reached, exploitation would be stopped and a new shaft sunk. The technological threshold of getting water out and drying headings was not crossed in ore mining until the mid-15th century. The Wieliczka deposits contain relatively little water (though because of salt's solubility it is more of a hazard here); the deeper and more extended headings called for more careful lining and more complex systems for output hauling.

The major obstacle in sinking a shaft down to a deposit at Wieliczka was a layer of soggy glacial clays. This semi-liquid, subsiding mass was overcome by the "lost-shaft" method, i.e. by first sinking a narrow hole — less than a metre wide — and carefully timber-lining it. The miners tried to condense these clays using straw or by draining off water. It was only afterwards that they reamed the hole and put in proper lining. The whole operation was very labour-consuming and took a lot of experience; at times two ever-wider "lost shafts" had to be sunk one by one so as to get through the dangerous layer. The layers of clays would sometimes take the better of the miners — such was the case in the 17th century with Wieliczka's "Ligęza" shaft which gave in to the pressure of the subsiding mass.

Salt blocks occur at Wieliczka already at depth between a dozen and several dozen metres. In 1790, for instance, during the sinking of the "Josef" (today "Kościuszko") shaft, salt was struck a mere 15 m. underground; in 1640 the "Daniłowicz" (so named after the then master of the salt mine) shaft got at fairly large resources at 24 m. deep — they were worked for several years as the "Włodkowice" chamber. The first shafts, however, went a little further down — to about 40 metres. From there, the underground headings began to extend horizontally. With the passage of time the distance between the headings and the shaft grew and so did haulage and ventilation problems. These were solved by "opening a new mountain" (a "mountain" was the name of a shaft together with the headings). In this way new salt resources were tapped and at the same time — by connecting two shafts with underground galleries — the routes of output haulage were cut short and air circulation ensured. This natural ventilation proved its worth fully. The first mechanical ventilator pumping air into the mine was not installed until 1924. Earlier on, artificial airing was used only exceptionally, in sinking shafts and in long, blind prospecting galleries. As the mine expanded, special galleries and fore-shafts would be made to keep up the circulation of air. For it so happened in the 17th and 18th centuries that the lack of oxygen and saturation of the air with rock and salt dust made exploitation impossible, put out oil lamps, etc. The "Nadachów" chamber, for instance, was deep and abounded in green salt, "but the hewer did not mine it at such time because of the stuffiness that puts lights out".

40

The name of the first — dating from the 1280s — shaft probably derived from the name of the Cracow burgher, Gierasz, mentioned in the Wieliczka foundation act of 1290. He must have been one of the investors with whom the king concluded an agreement on shaft sinking. More Wieliczka mountains came about in the 1340s. These are: the "Świętosławska" (after the then treasurer Świętosław), the "Swadkowska" and the "Królewska" (or "Regis"). The shaft "Regis" was sunk in 1334; it has survived to this day as the only one of the four oldest and is serving as a ventilation shaft. It has been stripped of the characteristic hoist tower hence not every tourist knows that the stately building in the town centre opposite the "Wieliczka-Rynek" railway station houses the mouth of the ancient, good old shaft.

Till the beginning of the 16th century the Wieliczka mine was extended exclusively horizontally. Salt prospecting had been conducted with galleries running from the shafts' walls and bottoms, from worked-out chambers and galleries. The royal commissioners attached great importance to the prospecting works as they realized that early discovery of new resources was vital for the mine's existence. In charting the direction of prospecting for salt blocks erratically scattered in the deposit, the Wieliczka miners had their own experience and intuition for all to go by. Careful observations were made of the stratification of the green-salt blocks exploited and guidance was provided by the course of the salt radii (cracks in the block-holding loams filled with salt). The approach to a block was signalled by the appearance of loams including lots of single salt crystals. The galleries "followed the salt", describing arcs and curves, rising and falling in line with the salt seams and sub-seams. With time, this had produced a veritable labyrinth of twisting, capriciously winding galleries connecting the working chambers.

The first breakthrough in the mine's development took place in the early 16th century. Thanks to a meticulous inventory drawn up in 1518 by Stanisław Tarnowski commissioned by Jan Boner, today we have fairly detailed knowledge about the mine's appearance at the time. We know that at that time the extraction shafts were the "Regis" and the "Seraf" shafts sunk in 1442; the others served as ventilators and timber would be lowered down them or water brought up. Salt was hewn from 25 chambers. The Tarnowski inventory also lists several internal fore-shafts running from the first mine level inside the formation. The stage of storeyed expansion of the headings, i.e. the opening of new salt resources, had thus been ushered in.

The mine's storeyed expansion had still another important aspect: it constituted a great stride towards a knowledge of the deposit's structure. So far its upper portion had been worked — blocks of coarse-grain green salt; the first internal fore-shafts got down to the level at which bed deposits occur at Wieliczka. The Wieliczka miners got to know new sorts of salt differing from the green salt in appearance, grain size and the way of occurring in the rock. One of those sorts was called "fore-shaft salt" (after the way it was discovered); there were two varieties of it: *oczkowata* (eyelet) and *orłowa* (eagle). The latter — very pure and of medium-size grain — was intended exclusively for the royal table. It was loaded into barrels marked with the eagle emblem. Another variety was fine-grained, slightly sandy compact *spizowa* salt (from the Latin for dense — *spissus*).

The mine's expansion and ever more information about the deposit's structure necessitated the basing of mining-operation planning on more exact criteria than the experience and intuition of the old hewers. So in the 16th century measurements of the underground headings was started on a larger scale, using qualified surveyors. The distances were measured by the foreman's stick and string, the directions for the galleries' course were determined by compass. Towards the end of the century the royal surveyor, the Italian Pietro Franco, was active in the salt mines; later on "*montium sálinarum architector*" Jan Taubenheim put in an appearance at Wieliczka. In the years 1616—20 measurements down the mine were made by Jan Brożek, the mathematician, astronomer, historian of science and professor and rector at the Cracow Academy. In a letter to the mathematician Stanisław Pudłowski he wrote that he had acted "pro Republica, having often lowered myself cum magno vitae periculo at Wieliczka, at Bochnia for many years".

The author of the first plans preserved to this day was Marcin German, Swedish by origin, a foreman of the "Regis" mountain of long standing. In the years 1631—38 he made a plan of the town of Wieliczka and of the mine's three levels, marking on it the names of the chambers, galleries and shafts; the names of the owners of municipal land, etc. Detailed surveying has shown German's work as characterized by a surprising thoroughness, the errors not exceeding 1%. In the history of European mining-cartography German's work is predated only by plans of the salt mines in Hall (Tyrol, 1531), in Dürrenberg (in the Alps, 1535) and of the zinc mine in Altenberg (1574), the gold and silver mine at Tarnowskie Góry (1577) and the gold mine in Grakofel (1577).

The vertical expansion of the headings soon caused the Wieliczka miners considerable hauling troubles. Output had to be got out of a chamber first by the gallery to the nearest fore-shaft, hoisted on to a higher level, then again rolled along winding and narrow galleries to the next fore-shaft and on to the day-shaft connecting the first mine level with the surface. It was not until the mid-18th century that it was decided to deepen the day-shafts. The first to be deepened was the "Regis" shaft which in 1743 reached the third mine level, that is 130 metres. In the same year a prohibition was issued on extracting at the first level (salt had been mined there for 450 years!) which was a contributory reason why salt was searched for ever further and further down the deposit.

The times of the Austrian partition brought more changes in the mine's spatial layout. The Austrians put some order in the network of headings, running through them straight, criss-crossing galleries along (longitudinally) and across (transversally) the deposit. This made it possible to bring in more modern means of haulage. The cutting up of a deposit with a network of regular galleries was also of great importance for a more detailed knowledge of the geological structure. Towards the end of the 18th century from the old field of knowledge — hitherto called "natural history" — there began to separate geognosis — the science which provided the foundations of modern geology. Proof that there was interest in this new field were the Wieliczka "geognostic

42

cuts" showing a deposit in vertical cross-section and not as up till then — horizontal.

Today after 700 years of continuous operation the Wieliczka mine stretches over a length of close on 6 km., a width of 900 m. and a depth of 330 m. At the nine levels there are nearly two thousand worked-out chambers; down in the ground there are empty spaces totalling a volume of 7.5 million cu. m. left by the extraction of some 25 million tons of salt. The headings totalling a length of 300 km. can take visitors on a tour through the seven centuries of the history of the Polish salt from the 13th century to the year 1986, from the "Goryszow-ski" shaft to the currently-worked "Sułków" area.

A prospecting shaft having struck a salt block, the stage of readying it for exploitation began. A prospecting gallery was lengthened by hairpin bends steeply uphill in an effort to get at the block's tip. Only there was a horizontal gallery tunnelled, from the walls of which salt was mined. Both during the tunnelling of the gallery and after, during salt hewing, the miners had to take care not to break through the block-encasing loams and just leave a layer of salt some two metres thick to keep the heading from caving in. The approach to the block's periphery was announced by the picks striking the wall giving off a muffled sound and by loamy lodes coming into view, etc.

The method of salt-hewing did not change from the mines' beginning right down to the 20th century. In the wall or floor of a chamber miners hacked grooves some 60 cm. deep around the block to be torn off. Such a cuboid-shaped block was usually 120 cm. wide and 360—720 cm. long. Next, one of the grooves was widened so that iron wedges could go in.

The hewing off of blocks called for considerable experience and skills. The course of the salt layers had to be reckoned with, the wedges had to be inclined at the correct angle and driven in carefully and evenly, the block to be torn off had to be well supported so that, weighing perhaps 10 tonnes, once loose from the wall, it did not break. Especially difficult was work in narrow deposits where miners often had to hack grooves in the surrounding stone.

Once broken loose from the wall, a salt block was divided into parts which were subsequently worked to make them into barrel-shaped lumps. Their size and weight differed in different periods. In the 16th century, for instance, three kinds of lump were manufactured: the Cracow block (900 kg.), the Oświęcim lump (1000 kg.) and the Slovak block (600 kg.). In the 17th century Wieliczka supplied the market with as many as nine sorts of lump. Some of these weighed 2,200—2,500 kg.

Apart from the blocks, the Cracow salt mines manufactured salt in the form of smaller, irregular blocklets obtained from blocks fractured during gallery-tunnelling, and during the working of narrow deposits. These blocklets were sold by weight. Fine salt was loaded into barrels and used only as raw material in salt-panning.

The first changes in the above system of deposit working did not come until Austrian times. These were foreshadowed as early as in 1772 by the introduction of the blasting method — for the moment only in gallery-tunnelling. A hundred years later the first attempts were made at Wieliczka to cut grooves around a block using circular cutters powered by compressed air; block-loosening, however, continued to be done by the old system of wedge-driving. The Austrians changed also the assortment of the salt mined: the lumps were gradually taken out of manufacture and replaced by regular salt cubes weighing some 50 kg.

HOW A DIGGER
HEWED SALT

DOGS, HORSES AND TREADMILLS

The bringing of output to the surface was for a long time one of the major problems for the Wieliczka miners. In the 17th century there was one salt-hewer per ten men dealing with the haulage of the lumps and barrels. At first the hauling was done along the old prospecting galleries — winding, narrow and uneven. Starting from the 16th century special hauling galleries and fore-shafts were made but real order was not made in the communications lines until the advent of "longitudinals" and "transversals" during Austrian times. During the same period the galleries' bumpy floor was inlaid with thick box-tree for easier rolling of the carts. The first rails on the underground hauling routes were not put in at Wieliczka until 1861.

Lumps were rolled along the galleries by hand, levered with strong wooden poles. From the end of the 18th century the output was hauled in narrow carts whose wooden wheels gave off sounds like barking — hence they were called dogs. Fine salt was carried from the headings on back in all sorts of bags to chambers where it was rammed into barrels and these in turn were lugged along to the shaft on a sort of sled. At first the sleds were drawn by men; horses were "employed" underground in the 16th century.

The horses make a chapter apart of the mining story. They were great favourites at all times, which is best proved by the carefully fitted out and beautifully-adorned underground stables. In olden times whinnying could be heard down the mine fairly often; today only two have remained there: Kuba and Drab. They live 170 m. underground and are irreplaceable in hauling materials needed for protecting old headings. In the maze of old galleries modern technology is losing out to the four legs of a horse... These animals are often the subject of miners' anecdotes which have perpetuated the individualities and traits of some horse characters. Memories are still alive of Kary, an exceptionally gregarious horse who used to stop his minder in the stable after work by cleverly obstructing his way out — the only rescue being a ransom in the shape of a slice of bread. Another of these four-legged employees would catch the working men off their guard and ease packed lunches out of the pockets of jackets left lying about. So deft was he at it that it was not until after quite some time that he was caught red-handed — or red-mouthed, rather. Many horses had become accustomed to a fixed number of carts; if a heavier-than-usual weight had been hitched on they struck and would not move. It is being said down the mine to this day that "even the horse knows his norm and counts the carts..."

Let us get back to the old times, though. Ever since the salt mines came into being, attempts were made to apply here all sorts of wooden gear to help in hauling weights along galleries and in hoisting them up fore-shafts. The oldest and simplest of such gear were windlasses with a horizontal shaft round which a rope wound. The shafts were turned round using crosswise poles either passed through them or set at their ends and fitted with gripping-spokes on their circumference. Towards the end of the 16th century Wieliczka saw the first of a structure based on the principle of a vertical shaft with a rope-reel set on it. The shaft was turned round by pushing the poles put through holes in it; the drive was provided by man power or horses. The "Hungarian" and the "Saxon" treadmills introduced into the mine in the 18th century were engineered on the same principle. The arm-span of those machines was up to 12 m. and they were worked by 8—12 horses. Earlier on, from the beginning of the 17th century, Wieliczka used "Polish" treadmills of a little more complex design. Horses turned round a horizontal wheel with — on their circumference — pegs engaging the spokes of another, vertical wheel fixed to the hoist shaft. This type of treadmill exhibited at the Cracow Salt Mines Museum, was in operation in the 18th century over the "Daniłowicz" shaft. It was powered by four pairs of horses, lifted weights from a depth of 65 m. and its lifting capacity was 2.5 tonnes. The treadmills were fitted with brakes (wooden jaws clamped to a shaft-set wheel by a system of levers), rollers and wheels guiding the rope and changing the direction of its course. The 18th century saw the application of two ropes so wound on the shaft that as one rose the other dropped. At the same time braking gear for lowering weights down inclined drifts and fore-shafts were put in underground. Steel ropes appeared at Wieliczka in the mid-19th century; earlier, lime-tree bast or hemp ropes were used. The 1860s saw the first steam hoist machine over the "Regis" shaft; the last treadmill worked over the "Boża Wola" shaft till 1881.

The collection of wooden hoist gear exhibited at the Cracow Salt Mines Museum today arouses understandable interest among the historians of technology. Such machines were used in the whole of Europe centuries ago, for building castles and cathedrals, putting up columns and monuments, lifting bells onto church towers, and loading cargo in ports. Today it is only from descriptions and iconographic records that we know about them since, exposed to the action of atmospheric factors and attacked by wood-eaters, the machines have long ago disintegrated. They only survived at Wieliczka where, impregnated with brine and kept in a "sterile" atmosphere, timber is fully resistant to bacteria, fungi, dry rot, etc.

Hoist gear — apart from output haulage and lowering men — also served for removing water from headings. Salt's solubility made water into a formidable enemy of the Wieliczka miners, hence the great importance that has long been attached to bringing it up onto the surface.

One source of mine waters are atmospheric precipitations, streams and rivulets — or surface water collecting over the salt deposit. Natural protection against these is afforded by the overlaying stratum of impervious Chodenice loams. Over these, the glacial-clay stratum stops surface waters and the layer of soggy glacial clays, that we have talked of above, is thus formed. Man's activities (shaft sinking, cave-ins of worked-out chambers) cause the impervious loam stratum to crack and water to penetrate the salt deposits. Luckily for Wieliczka the surface water network is rather poor here, which makes deposit-mining possible as long as underground effluxes are spotted in time and the watercourses down the mine controlled.

Water flowing from walls was collected in vats and channelled off by wooden piping and gutters. The raising of water on to a higher level was either by hand (with scoops from vat to vat) or using bucket-wheels, and from the 18th century — pendulum pumps. In this respect Wieliczka did not use the rich experiences of the ores mines. This was probably due to the fact that the machines for draining those mines had a large number of metal parts which in contact with the chemically active brine were soon destroyed.

Waters from the headings were directed to carefully-lined and tar-sealed receptacles at the bottoms of the shafts. Thence they were brought up in huge bags made from ox-hides sewn together. For a long time at Wieliczka a special shaft ("Wodna" or "Surowicza Góra") was intended exclusively for bringing up water. It was first mentioned in 1381 — and it was out of operation in 1866. It received effluxes from the whole of the mine by a system of gutters and piping; often, however, the excessive waters had to be brought up by output shafts.

THE WET ENEMY

In the 16th century (it should be recalled that this was a period of a decline in salt-making) water began to be collected in worked-out chambers. Miners were under the illusion that by adding fine salt to such receptacles they would be able to saturate the solution and that it would thus not dissolve the receptacles' salt walls. This theoretically correct assumption did not work in practice. That, over a time, created large receptacles threatening with flooding headings in the event of a chamber cave-in. The problem grew worse especially in the 18th century when the hauling routes were being put in order and new galleries tunnelled in old parts of the mine. Miners would come on such forgotten chambers. In 1772, the Austrian mine administrators ordered that on two days in any week only water should be brought up by all the shafts. In the 1840s some 5,000 tonnes of water a year was "brought up into the world."

In the early 19th century a simple but efficient method of removing water from flooded chambers was applied. From a gallery under such a chamber a hole was drilled and then stopped up with a tapped wooden bung. This made possible controlled water outflow and channelling it off to a shaft's bottom.

Another, much more dangerous, source of mine waters are the water-logged overlying strata which form a sort of huge underground receptacle bordering on the salt deposit in the North and dating from the period of the last glaciation (more than 25,000 years ago). A breaking through the impervious strata separating them from the mine can cause a sudden inrush of huge masses of water into the headings.

Wieliczka had a foretaste of such a catastrophe in 1868 when despite geologists' warnings the decision was made to prospect for salt in a northern direction. On Thursday, 19 November, from a hole drilled in the "Wolskie" gallery water began to issue. The salt-mining commission called in by the miners decided that the outflow was not dangerous and ordered the water channelled off in gutters to a shaft. Three days later, on a Sunday, water overflowed the fixed gutters and began to flood the gallery. The mine's administration tried to keep that secret but news of it had already got about in town, causing concern among the inhabitants. Crowds of people began to gather in front of the "Regis" shaft (called the "Franz Josef" shaft at the time) and of the "Wodna Góra" whence the roar of falling water could be heard. The Wieliczka authorities appealed for quiet and composure. The senior mining counsellor Balascic arrived in Wieliczka and took over as head of the rescue operation.

At first attempts were made to stop the outflow with sandbags but the water-current had grown so strong that it swept them along into the mine. There was no coming closer to the outflow because of the carbon dioxide emission. In this situation it was necessary to wall up the exploratory shaft exit into the "Kloski" chamber. Because of the cramped conditions only three people could work at a time; they were relieved every two hours. The wall was ready at the end of three days and nights of uninterrupted work on 1 December at 7 a.m. Four hours later the water, having dissolved the salt walls around the dam, rushed forth again. Another dam was put up which proved no better than the first. The "Wodna Góra" sump was full; water had flooded the whole of the sixth level of the mine. The salt pillar supporting the huge "Kloski" chamber (the ceiling of which reached the first level and the floor of which was at the fifth level) began to dissolve and the wooden crib in the same chamber was undermined and collapsed. As the "Kloski" chamber spread under Wieliczka's Lower Market Place with the church and castle, catastrophe threatened the town's very centre.

Luckily, the water level down the mine stopped rising — a cave-in inside the strata having stopped the outflow. Steam machines were installed over three Wieliczka shafts and for several months, day and night, water was pumped out. The people of Wieliczka were uneasy right to the end of the operation. Knowledge of the deposit's geological structure at the time was too poor for it to be absolutely ascertained that the water had come from a post-glacial receptacle. Rumours spread around the town that it was the waters of the Vistula that had rushed into the mine by underground corridors and that Wieliczka was faced with complete destruction.

Water was not the only enemy of the miners. Like all mines, Wieliczka was threatened with cave-ins by the overlaying strata. The hard shields of green salt surrounding empty worked-out places may have been fairly good protection against crushing but the vast spaces of Wieliczka chambers, errors in the mining technique (for example, the leaving of a too thin layer of salt) and the action of the waters penetrating the mine compelled the application of various systems for heading-lining. That was of great importance especially in mining the less resistant deposit salts. The royal commissioners used to warn that in pursuit of profits, extraction should not be increased at all cost, human lives not exposed and the mine's technical state not worsened. The minutes of one of the weekly conferences read:

"According to the old custom and the regulations read out I hereby admonish foremen to see to it that dangerous places where the Treasury would stand more to lose are not worked and that, wherever necessary, salt pillars be left to support the firmament..."

One way of securing the mine was to leave protective pillars in places especially exposed to the strata pressure. A continuous battle went on for their preservation between the supervisers and the thoughtless miners. The latter, interested in getting their salt allowances, searched for the easiest places with fine salt and, in contravention of the prohibitions, would undercut the pillars. In 1710 commissioners reported having found "impaired salt pillars at which miners have been espied picking, ignoring the mine master's crosses (a cross marked a prohibited salt-mining place, finished segments of works, etc. "so that a cross keeps a digger from cheating"). The results of the unruly miners' activities could be seen, for example, in 1642 in the "Panewnik" chamber where "the middle and breast of the pillar are very thick... but it is undercut and so picked-at by wanton workers that it rests as if only on fingers". The enormous danger that pillar-undercutting posed to the mine led in 1625 to the imposition of the penalty of cutting off hands for this offence. Thirteen years later indeed, two miners·were sentenced to this but — as far as we know — the punishment was never carried out.

Another — more frequent even than the pillars — way of securing the headings were cribs or layers of trunks laid alternately and wedged under the ceiling. A crib took thoroughness and experience to build. It also took enormous quantities of timber: for the building of a crib in one of the chambers might use 8,260 trunks; the ceiling of the today inaccessible "Przykos" chamber was once supported by a crib 36 m. wide and 105 m. high. No wonder then that the extension of the mine led to a fall in salt-panning; supplying timber for the protection of the headings against cave-ins was plainly more important than using it for fuel in the salt-works.

The system of protecting the headings by using pillars and cribs was the only one to be used right down to the beginning of the 20th century. In 1836 the first trials were made and only in 1902 was the backfilling system — i.e., filling in the threatened chambers with sand brought down from the surface — actually used on a larger scale.

FIRE, VAPOURS
AND SALTPETRE

The cribs effectively resisted the strata pressure and in this respect performed their task well. This, however, was related to a danger of another sort: the accumulation of a great amount of timber meant that every fire was a veritable disaster for the mine. It has to be borne in mind that till the 20th century the only sources of light underground were, first, open-flame oil lamps — initially tallow, from 1839 oil — and then carbide ones. The causes of the fires were diverse; indeed at times an unguarded moment was enough.

Such was the case on 15 December 1644 when workers dumping hay for the horses working underground down a shaft inadvertently swept along a few embers from a nearby bonfire. The hay caught fire and an explosion ensued which threw the roof of the building over the shaft-head a few dozen metres away. The fire soon spread into 16 chambers. The cribs and gallery lining were ablaze, methane pockets exploded, and unpropped headings collapsed. An unsuccessful fight against the fire lasted for a few months and several dozen people died. In spring 1645 the cave-in reached ground level and houses began to subside. Smoke was coming out of all the shafts, funeral cortèges went along Wieliczka's streets incessantly and the frightened inhabitants left their homes and bivouacked in the surrounding hills.

The 1696 fire broke out in a wooden chapel in the "Boczaniec" chamber. Old documents say that during the night foreman Marcin Czaiński and guard Grzegorz Dobrzański went down the mine. They lit candles in the altar of the "Boczaniec" chamber and went into the mine to plan work for the following day. It was probably from a candle flame that the paper and wooden decorations of the altar caught fire. An air current kept the fire alive and before long it spread to the cribs and the wooden lining of the galleries. The fire lasted for a whole year; during the following "six Sundays" the mine had to be vented because smoke made going down impossible. The mine authorities conducted an investigation into the causes of the fire and did not find "that somebody should be punished, it having been put down to misadventure, yet the late Czaiński, out of apprehension and great disturbance, died suddenly in the bath".

The fire in the "Boczaniec" chamber also caused a surface cave-in; the first to collapse were the "Słabaczów" and "Zgłobice" chambers and then the ground complete with the buildings subsided near the "Górsko" shaft. And the inhabitants of one of those buildings experienced a rather unusual adventure. The incident happened at night, and the house was subsiding so slowly and evenly that the people sleeping inside did not notice anything. When they woke up in the morning they had to go onto the roof and only from there climb ladders to the brink of a huge hole into which their house had sunk.

Rescue operations down a blazing mine called for courage and devotion. The cramped underground headings were filled with choking smoke, the treacherous carbon monoxide struck people unconscious, the methane pockets exploded with a loud bang and caused panic; the mine echoed with the boom of breaking side walls and collapsing chambers. One such operation was described by the Wieliczka surveyor, Antoni Frydhuber. In the night of 6 April 1772 the men working underground smelled smoke — the crib in the "Adamów" chamber was ablaze. An hour later the then administrator Wojciech Kluszewski and deputy mine master Jan Kiełczewski came over the "Daniłowicza" shaft.

Kluszewski organized a rescue operation while Frydhuber and Kiełczewski went down trying to get through to the fire. The underground, however, had been so filled with smoke that they could not see a lighted oil lamp from five steps. Men went down also by other shafts to check — as long as the "vapours" permitted — whether anybody had been left in the danger area and watchers were posted to report on the development of the situation. Having checked that nobody had remained in the headings they set about putting up dams (terraces) to cut off air from the blaze area. The shafts' openings were boarded up and sealed with dung and earth. The following day at noon Frydhuber was informed that the dams were leaking the murderous carbon monoxide. The surveyor lost no time getting to the mine. He did not manage to get to the dam, though, and carbon monoxide had rendered unconscious the dare-devils who had tried to. In this situation the surveyor decided to put up another dam, closer to the shaft, in order to stop the "vapours". The work was not completed owing to the quickly-rising concentration of carbon monoxide. Miners were able to work two-hours stints at the most and were so weakened that they had to be carried out afterwards into the shaft. Even the horses hauling over materials fell from the poisonous gas. It was not until the umpteenth time round that they succeeded in finishing the job and cut off the "vapours". However, the carbon monoxide soon began to seep through the other dams so that the whole operation had to be repeated in other galleries.

On 8 April the openings of the "Janina" and "Leszno" shafts were uncovered. For a time "stinking smoke which kept both people and beasts away" issued from it. With the fumes gone, Frydhuber tried to go down by the "Leszno" shaft. The shaft, sunk in 1651, was the only one in the Cracow salt mines to be circular in cross-section and have stone steps. The miners preceding the surveyor opened the door leading from the shaft to the first level. After a while Frydhuber's oil lamp blew off and he himself suddenly began to swoon. At the same time he heard men below shout for help. He began to flee up the steps. "My breath grew shorter and shorter, I ran a great fever and began to retch; there was now no way I could go up a single step more." His cries for help were heard by deputy master Kiełczewski who ran down the shaft and carried out the swooning surveyor. The miners in the shaft top hastened to the aid of their colleagues.

It was not until after a week that you could enter the "Adamów" chamber. Just a single crib had burnt down, the other three having been left intact. The chamber's ceiling and walls had partially collapsed. The salt from the fallen ceiling later filled 15,000 barrels. Those were the results of just a single crib in the Wieliczka mine catching fire...

No wonder then that the mine regulations were particularly concerned with the prevention of fires. Guards appointed to police the underground were to see to it that oil lamps were put out in the chapels after work, that men handled their oil lamps with care and they were to punish workers for smoking tobacco down the mine. After the fire in the "Boczaniec" chamber the royal commissioners who happened to be in Wieliczka at the time and had been able to see for themselves what danger was posed by a fire started underground, ordered all the wooden altars removed from the chambers and let only those hewn in the body of salt remain. They also prohibited decking altars with paper, fir twigs, and the like. They permitted the lighting of candles only during divine services; during work time only tallon lamps (these played a practical as well as religious role: they let men re-kindle their oil lamps blown out by an air current) were allowed in front of the shrines.

In 1747 special fire regulations were drawn up binding not only on the miners but also on all the inhabitants of the town. In 34 items they discuss problems of prevention (household heads, for example, being ordered "not to allow, especially children, to walk about with flaming candles without a lantern or with live embers"), set up night guards, ordered the keeping of fire-fighting equipment (vats, jugs, pails with water, fire-hooks, ladders, and the like), and deal with the organization of rescue operations.

Another hazard to the Wieliczka miners — apart from flooding, cave-ins and fires — was "saltpetre" or methane. This gas imprisoned under great pressure in the pockets in the strata is especially dangerous in combination with the air. It creates an explosive mixture that blows up on contact with fire. With a pocket pierced during mining works, methane hisses free and — since it is lighter than air — accumulates under the ceiling. For whole centuries there was in the Cracow salt mines a special group of miners dealing with methane burning. They were always the first to go down and — covered with soaked canvases — crawled along the floor of the headings holding a stick topped with a blazing wisp of straw aloft. The methane accumulated under the ceiling would explode and the rest of the staff could then safely set about their work. Fortunately, there is little methane in the Wieliczka deposit in comparison with other mines: the pocket found during the deepening of the "Gruszczyn" foreshaft in 1762 was an absolute exception. The gas which issued in great quantities kept burning for several months until the pocket emptied completely. It was not possible safely to detect methane's presence until the introduction in 1819 of the Davy lamp, which is being used in Wieliczka to this day.

Men

Today it is stillness and darkness that reign in the Wieliczka mine's old headings, neither the hubbub of the visiting groups pressing in the Museum's chambers nor the boom of the machinery from the areas currently in operation getting through to here. A careful look around, however, is enough for the underground headings to reveal the shadows of those who once created the shape of the salt walls: a wooden shrine at the intersection of galleries, an awkward inscription on a crib, a broken pickaxe haft with a handle polished with human palms, and a side wall with a cross, date and names of those who never went up out "into the world".

It is only those human traces that put some sense into this underground wilderness and darkness. Without them the Wieliczka mine would just be an absurd hole in the earth; its value would be equal to the price of the salt that it once contained. Indeed, attempts have been made to apply such a yardstick to Wieliczka and the calculation produced one conclusion: the mine is not needed, it has to be shut down...

But Wieliczka is lucky in its people. There have always been accountants who have added to the price of salt in the Wieliczka balance sheet the value of human thought, the price of the sweat, blood and lives of whole generations of miners. The results of their sums have grown into a monument not to nature but to man.

The workers of the Cracow salt mines have always composed a rather exceptional staff. This stems from the singular status of a "state enterprise" that the mines have been entitled to ever since they came into existence.

"His Royal Majesty's miners" worked here and although in practice the road to the king was very long their knowledge of their exceptional standing in the social structure has until the present day been fairly strong. The mining trade was entered by free people (in contradiction to the Russian salt industry where much of the work was done by serfs) with no capital, means of production or any rights to the commodity turned out (unlike in ore mining). The rights and duties of the particular worker groups were strictly defined by the royal regulations; the enterprise's organizational model had inbuilt checks protecting the employee against the arbitrariness of and exploitation by his superiors. The great numerical strength of the staff and the difficult working conditions which called for self-dependence and made supervision over the workers an easy task helped to make the Cracow salt mines — as early as in the 14th century — look more like an early-capitalist than a feudal enterprise.

Cracow-area miners knew, if need be, how to vindicate their rights and very high up, too. During the wages quarrel in 1592 the Bochnia diggers sent a delegation to the king himself; the chamberlain negotiated with them on his behalf. Occasions to air grievances and make petitions were provided by the regular visits to the mines by commissions whose members were bound by the royal regulations to contact simple workers and to hear out their complaints. For example, in 1670 the commissioners wrote, "We have been asked for higher wages by the workers of the Bochnia salt mine; and we, commissioners of His Royal Majesty, having considered the toil of the local worker and having regard to the expensiveness of foodstuff items, in order to make him more willing and obedient, hereby recommend that the Bochnia salt mine should pay the bearers, diggers, crushers and other underground workers in genere 1 and 1/2 zlotys." Appropriate recommendations guaranteeing workers' rights were also contained in the contracts of lease. "Employees should be paid without delay or negligence whenever they might work" — ordered Ladislaus Jagiello in an agreement concluded with Antonio and Leonardo Florentino in 1425.

A great role in the defence of the employees' interests was played by the fraternities for diggers (associating salt-hewing workers) and bearers (haulage employees). The fraternities' elders had the right of say in taking on labour and in fixing wage rates, took part in production conferences and also had certain powers of jurisdiction.

The mines' administration realized that the singular working conditions in the mines ruled out the use of violence against the workers. Regulations for the officials said that if they "choose to further the works by command and violence, then a lot of harm and little good is to be expected". The 1650 list of duties of the Wieliczka mine deputy master contained, among other things, these recommendations: "Recognize the friendliness of the foremen who, if they feel like it, do harm"; "Talk with clerks and elder workers about how best to run the underground works" etc. Workers could not be used for work in favour of the officials. No clerk could punish an employee by taking away part of his pay without the written order of the mine's "director" himself. The loyalty of the officials employed in the salt mines was enlisted with oaths.

The first Wieliczka miners must have come from the community of the local salt panners and specialists — Germans and Germanized Silesians. Towards the end of the 13th century Italians and Frenchmen also put in an appearance here. The German population disappeared from Wieliczka as early as the beginning of the 14th century — expelled by King Ladislaus the Short after the rebellion of Albert, *scultetus* of Cracow. Another German wave did not come until the times of the Saxon dynasty and later during the Austrian rule; this time, however, the Germans were almost exclusively senior administrative and technical officials of the mine.

The number of those employed changed constantly depending on relations in the state and the stages in the mine's expansion. At times of labour shortages attempts were made to attract those who were known as "loose" people to Wieliczka. For example, in 1565 the king prohibited the Bochnia municipal authorities (which, given the more difficult working conditions, used to have more troubles making up its staff) to stop those willing to take up work in the mine from settling. The salt mines even protected serfs escaped from villages. When in 1625 a certain Piotr Borzychowski demanded that one of his men be handed over to him, he was told that the peasant in question worked in a royal mine and could not be delivered without the agreement of the monarch. All sorts of other means fairly well known to us also from later times were used to obtain labour. Augustus II in 1720 excused miners from doing national service; the Emperor Joseph II enfranchised peasants from the surrounding villages; the mine's Austrian board bought near-by land and allotted small plots to new miners, also granting credit for building their own houses. The Cracow-area mines did not employ convicts which was due to the too great risk of arson or devastation of the headings. The only cases known to us of prisoners' working there were during the tenure as salt-mine master of Jan Odrowąż Pieniążek (1670—72) and the period of the Nazi occupation.

Whenever labour was in over-abundant supply priority in employment was given to inhabitants of Wieliczka and Bochnia. This gave certain guarantees of a stable staff and possibilities of controlling the employees. Also the municipal authorities had an interest there; newcomers "when some burden falls on these towns, having taken their bundles ... flee". It was also from among Wieliczka burghers and local landed gentry that the mines' officials and technical staff were drawn; the influx of specialists from other mining centres was, considering the mine's geologically specific character, insignificant.

The dangerous and responsible work in the mine called for both skills and appropriate moral values. The principle — formulated in the 1592 royal regulations — was especially observed that "*nemo potest duobus dominis servire, et Regi et Bacho*" — you cannot serve two masters, the king and Bacchus. Drunken workers were kept out of the mine and the smuggling of vodka below ground carried harsh penalties. Also punishable was misconduct outside the place of employment. Dishonest workers would be sacked so that "they do not have to be suffered by the royal worker" and did not bring the royal miners' good name into disrepute. Also punishable were swearing, gossiping, quarrels, "indecent words". A worker who had stolen something from his mate, apart from being punished by his superior, stood trial by his workmates — they were to decide "whether they are willing to suffer a man that has sinned against them in their midst at work".

DIGGERS
AND BEARERS

The Wieliczka mine's staff was divided into three groups: the underground miners, the salt-mine apprentices or men employed on the surface, and the administrative clerks and technical personnel — or the officials. In the first group a privileged position — owing to their high qualifications — was enjoyed by the diggers who hewed salt blocks.

In the initial period of the Cracow mines' existence the king, wishing to attract specialists to a newly-established mining centre, would confer on them a privilege consisting in a guaranteed workplace. The privilege was for ever, the king being obliged, the salt having been mined out from a given place, to ensure another. The privilege was hereditary; it could be donated, pledged or sold to another person or institution. That right was used very early on — as early as the beginning of the 14th century such privileges were held by monasteries, hospitals and royal officials. In the mine they were replaced by hired workers who shared their earnings with the privilege holders. At first the number of such privilege holders was limited to sixty: Casimir the Great in a 1368 statute explained that if they had been more then "the mounts would the sooner empty themselves of salt". It was not until Wieliczka salt was found to last a great many generations that the number of privileges increased to 121 in the 18th century. The Saxon administration in 1728 did away with the privileges, replacing them with perpetual rents.

As the mine expanded successive mining specialities arose. The tunnelling of exploratory galleries has already been discussed; in a later period tunnelling workers dealt with (apart from salt prospecting) also tunnelling haulage galleries, hewing out chambers for treadmills and other hoisting machines. The other miners were employed in hewing crazy salt blocks hanging from the ceiling or the walls. Traces of their activities are visible to this day in most of the Wieliczka mine's chambers; it was their pickaxes that left a fine grid of shallow grooves in the side walls. These portions of the deposit, which because of the impurities or small size were not suited for production of big blocks, were the concern of another group of hewers who produced fine barrel salt.

The most numerous group among the Wieliczka miners was always made up of hauling workers. As the hoisting gear improved old specialities disappeared and new ones arose among that group of workers. Some bearers worked the crosses, spoke wheels, etc. and others rolled blocks from a chamber to the shaft: still others hauled fine salt. A very responsible job was that of making loads fast to the treadmill's rope and working the hoisting gear. Of great importance for the mine's safety was the work of a special group of workers who dealt with scooping water gathered in the headings. After horses had been brought into the mine minding those animals was another job there.

The great number of jobs related to timber working caused a fairly narrow specialization among the timberers. Some of them dealt with the construction of pipes, gutters and vats making up water ducts, others repaired shaft lining and still others mended the treadmills, ladders, etc. Underground, guards were also employed who issued tools, saw to it that order was kept, put out lamps in the shrines after work, etc., as well as coopers who mended and closed barrels with salt rum. In the 18th century the function was established of candlers who lit the way underground for the mine's officials. They occupied the lowest rung in the underground workers' occupational hierarchy; the miners saw serving the officials as a detraction from their honour.

The mine's apprentices saw to the safety of the men going down and checked whether workers leaving the mine were not taking out salt, issued portions of tallow for lighting, and minded salt stores. There were also cobblers (sewing and mending of leather bags for scooping water), stable men, guards, smiths, etc.

All that numerous and motley staff was managed by the clerks. The whole of the mine was administered by the deputy mine master, one for Wieliczka and one for Bochnia. His "right hand man" was the scribe who kept the

enterprise's accountancy and reporting. Supplies were the concern of the dispenser who was responsible for the purchase of materials needed in production, foodstuffs for the mine kitchen, etc. The weighman supervised the loaders and dealt with reckoning the quantity and weight of the output brought up to the surface.

In the technical staff the top occupational standing was held by the foremen. Each of them had one mount, i.e. a working shaft complete with its headings, to look after. The foreman had overall technical supervision, measured progress in the diggers' work, and minded the hauling of output. The work of the shafts — getting up the output and the men's safety — was the responsibility of the headmen. The clerks included also employees who took from miners as they came to the surface their measures of fine salt.

In the first years of their existence the Cracow salt mines worked only in the winter, from September or November to the turn of May and June. Towards the end of the 14th century also what are known as royal weeks were introduced so that, should demand for salt rise, miners could be called to report for work also outside the scheduled period. From the beginning of the 16th century the mines worked all year round, and a hundred years later also around the clock, on a three-shift basis. Daywork mostly lasted eight hours of which seven were clear working hours while the eighth was spent in going down, getting to the chamber — which could be rather far from the shaft — and getting back. There have been periods, however (early 20th century) during which owing to the labour shortage workers were being forced to stay down the mine for as long as 10—14 hours.

For the royal miners the day began early in the morning. The royal regulations said: "Since a pious life is the foundation of all good, it is recommended that all miners live in fear of God, observe Sundays and feasts and begin the working days also with God, that is with mass which is said daily at five a.m. in the church specially founded for the miners by their majesties the Polish kings. Mass is to be heard every day by all miners yielding themselves to divine care and asking God to keep them from dangers so numerous in this difficult trade."

Then each miner took his portion of tallow. This was a very expensive material so it was meted out sparingly and care was taken to prevent abuses in this respect. The mine regulations laid down exactly how much tallow was to go to what workplace. Bearers who usually worked in groups and could use a single oil lamp received less tallow, the water scoopers — spattering drops putting out the flame more often — more, etc.

And finally it was time to go down. This moment of the Wieliczka miners' working day is known exceptionally well, constituting as it does the staple item of every description of the Cracow mines made by visitors to Wieliczka or Bochnia. It was here that many of them "where the shaft — dour like night — yawns with its open mouth", suddenly lost interest in the underground chambers and later described them on the basis of the information obtained from officials on the surface. We shall devote a little space to those descriptions in subsequent pages but now let us listen to Joachim Vadian, one of the more conscientious and credible authors.

In the shaft cage a huge treadmill with the horses hitched on is waiting. "From the machine hangs a huge-sized rope ... Those going down take saddles made of bast-string woven in their nether part like a plait and fastened to that huge rope; holding on to it with their hands and legs so that, suspended in this way, they do not swing in the air. For the most part, those suspended are lowered in pairs side by side — so that seven or even eight pairs hanging in succession go down ... Diggers, ... holding a lamp in one hand, use both legs to regulate the rope swinging in the great depth to stop it hitting the square-shaped oak-beam lining, or unbalancing those sitting too lightly and causing an accidental death." Indeed, a down-trip was none too safe and an "accidental death" was easy to cause. The mine regulations said that the workers "are not to press around the shaft on their way down or up; just five pairs go down ... carrying their pickaxes oil lamps and wedges carefully so as not to hit another under oneself", and pointed to the qualifications of the treadmill minders (they are to be people that are good, skilled, sober and sworn-in on whose sobriety and capabilities hangs the health of those going up or down).

In the underground chapel a collective prayer would be said. The mine's records take careful note of the special quantity of tallow earmarked daily "to the singing of the usual litanies before starting work... in the 'Lizak' ante iconem crucifixi Christi Domini." While the already-quoted information about mass in the parish church comes from as late as the mid-18th century the singing of "pious songs" on the way down and the daily prayer underground are mentioned already in the oldest descriptions of the Wieliczka miners' work. After prayer the workers went along the galleries and down the ladders in the internal foreshafts to their respective workplaces.

The regulations also obliged the officials to go down the mine frequently and regularly in order to control the progress of work. A 1650 document, for example, ordered the deputy mine master twice a week to visit each of the mounts: since they were three in Wieliczka at the time the "mine director" had to go down every day to inspect the underground headings since he would harm the royal interests "when unversed in the nether abysses he does not know anything about the works". The rigours for the lower-ranking clerks were, of course, still stiffer.

The coordination of the diverse activities of hundreds of people forced the elaboration as early as in the Middle Ages of an efficient system of information flow and internal auditing. This role was performed by the obligatory conferences of the mine clerks. Every evening the foremen met with the deputy mine master and fixed a work schedule for the following day. Major technical jobs (tunnelling of exploratory galleries, sinking of foreshafts, etc.) were discussed at conferences held every Thursday at 4 p.m. They were attended by: the deputy master, scribe, dispenser, surveyor, foremen and guards. The regulations said that "everybody is to perform his task according to his conscience and experience; the opinion of each shall be entered by the scribe in the minutes and in archivo conservare". On Sundays "ordinary trysts" attended by all the clerks were held; during these the newest orders and instructions were presented and the whole of the current problems of the enterprise discussed.

The specific production technology, the unique work tools and activities necessitated the framing of a number of notions and the coining of new terms; they gave a fair scope to the human imagination in word-coining. The chambers were often named after their characteristic features, colour or shape: "Biała Sień" (White Hallway), "Kręciny" (Windings), "Grzmiąca" (Thundering), "Korab" (Vessel), "Przykos" (Oblique; a chamber with oblique walls), "Liszki" (Fox Hole; narrow and winding like a fox hole), "Tanecznica" (Dancer; round, with an even floor), "Piaski" (Sands), "Skałka" (Little Rock), "Kisiałe Mleko" (Sour Milk; "no rock or salt, nothing but waste and loose mud", apparently like sour milk in consistency). The working conditions are bespoken by such names as "Dusząca" (Choking), "Pogorzelisko" (Site after fire). All sorts of conjectures are invited by "Krasna Anka" (Pretty Annie), "Suka" (Bitch), "Syberia" (Siberia) or "Oszust" (Swindler); some doubts are cast on the Wieliczka miners' model lives by the chamber called "Zamtuz" (Brothel)...

An interesting exception are the chambers made accessible to tourists; their names varied as did the political circumstances. For instance, the two eventually interlinked chambers, "Rosetti" and "Mayer", complete with a magnificent saline lake were called "Rudolf and Stephanie" during Austrian times, and "Józef Piłsudski" during the 20-year interwar period, nowadays known as the "General Karol Świerczewski Lake".

Linguistic inventiveness is with the mine's employees to this day: "czekolada" (chocolate) means loose, brown-coloured loam; "cykoria" (chicory) — an explosive stick whose shape and colour resembles the packaging of a once-popular chicory coffee made by the Franck firm; "jechać po ścirni" (to ride over stubble) — to push a dart along a rail-less gallery. Today's idiom of Wieliczka miners makes the most convincing — since impossible to fake — proof of the continuity of the mine's tradition. If today you ask the lift attendant how many times he still has to go up to take the staff to the surface, he will answer that he has got a number of "koniec" left. "Koniec" (end) is a word first recorded way back in the 1368 statute issued by Casimir the Great. It stood for the pulling up of the rope's end with a load attached to it onto the surface. The old regulations laid down the treadmill minders' norms as for the number of ends which have to be pulled up during a work day. The treadmill was later replaced with the electric hoist machine, the hemp ropes with a steel one, the winch seats with a metal cage, but a trace of history has remained in the jargon: you still pull up the "ends". The very process of bringing up output from the mine was termed in the Middle Ages "porekta" (from the Latin *porrectio* — pulling up). Today "porekta" means the loading in the salt-works of ready product into railway waggons. As in the old days so also today in Wieliczka you go up "into the world" (onto the surface), you load or handle "partyki" (shapeless salt lumps), etc.

"EXPOSED TO
A CERTAIN DEATH..."

For the wealth accruing to the Republic the Cracow salt mines exacted their toll of health and often of human life. The Venetian envoy Geronimo Lippomano wrote in 1575 that the Wieliczka miners were "exposed to a certain death from the huge salt blocks which sometimes come tumbling down, press down and kill many a man. It is strange that to replace those killed there is never a shortage of workers who for the pittance of a few groszys [pence] a day will take on work that clearly poses a danger to life. It was only criminals who used to be sentenced by the ancients to similar underground work". In the 17th century Claude Jordan wrote: "The workers blackened with smoke more resemble demons than people, while their workplace is a veritable hell, many getting buried in the salt since the poorly-supported ceilings often cave in."

Work in the mine was never safe. Especially during the tenure of dishonest lease-holders who disregarded the securing of headings, many miners lost their lives or became cripples because of cave-ins and accidents. Shrines can be seen in the mine's old sections to this day where once people died, or inscriptions cut in the side walls like this one: "Hence on 16 December 1863 the miners Jan Kaczorek, Józef Klejdysz, Jan Gluza went out and did not return. God, have mercy on them." In the 19th century the Wieliczka parish books often had such terse entries: "died from overwork," "crushed by a salt block", etc.

56

It has to be admitted that the royal enterprise took care of their employees by ensuring them from at least the mid-14th century free medical assistance and various forms of social welfare. In 1289 King Henry Probus founded a bath-house in Wieliczka (that, incidently, was the first establishment of this kind on Polish lands attested by documents). Bath-houses at the time were the preserve of barber-surgeons who performed simple operations: cupping, blood-letting, etc. From the mid-16th century a second bath-house — built and kept by the mine — was open.

In 1357 in Bochnia and six years later in Wieliczka the first hospitals were set up. They were founded by Casimir the Great at the request of salt-mine masters and the municipal authorities who, in a petition to the king, wrote that the miners "like exiles and orphans from all the corners of the world had come together and at work in the Bochnia mounts break their hands and legs as a result of accidents and they overtax their bodies so that they no longer can work and they suffer horribly since, once crippled, they have nowhere to put their heads and there is nobody to take care of them". It should be added here that a hospital at the time was not just a place for treatment (just as a bath-house was not exclusively for taking baths) but also a sort of poor-house giving cripples and old people shelter and food. The hospitals were maintained by the salt mine and their charges were mainly disabled miners. The Wieliczka hospital dedicated to the Holy Ghost was in the care of monks; it was shut down towards the end of the 18th century during the monastery-closing campaign by the Austrian authorities. Out of the funds and grants that the hospital had received arose the Holy Ghost Foundation intended for handouts to the accident-disabled or to widows and orphans of tragically-deceased employees. The foundations lasted till the outbreak of World War II. It must have been the only social-welfare programme run by an enterprise for the benefit of its employees for... almost six centuries on end.

The third — after the bath-house and the hospital — source of medical aid was the mine-employed *chirurgus*. The first information about him comes from 1499: it was recorded in the mine's books that the *chirurgus* had received 18 groszys for wound-dressing underground. Among the later "resident physicians" we meet several interesting figures. They included Anselmus Ephorinus, appointed physician of the royal mines by Sigismund Augustus in 1553. Ephorinus studied first at the Cracow Academy and then worked as a tutor to the sons of Jost Ludwik Decjusz and of Seweryn Boner. In 1531 he set off on a journey during which he established lively contacts with leading European humanists (Philipp Melanchton and Erasmus of Rotterdam, among them). As mine physician Ephorinus drew a fixed salary in return for which he was obliged to treat free of charge and supply medicines to the injured and ill miners. The salt-mine records show that he discharged his duties very well.

The mine's benefits were not limited to just medical help. An ill employee and his family had their upkeep ensured by being paid — almost from the beginning of the mine's existence — handouts and allowances. The royal regulations recommended that older employees should be transferred to lighter jobs. From the mid-17th century a fixed amount of money was earmarked to assist miners unable to work as well as widows and orphans of mine employees. It was shared out every three months by a special commission composed of deputy mine master, the salt-works master, foreman and scribe. This was the first permanent pension fund in Poland.

Another form of social welfare was the mine kitchen. Apart from the free breakfasts for the staff and food for the cart drivers it also fed poor and ill miners. The kitchen was shut down in 1565 and those entitled to its services were paid what was known as eating money. This "canteen" was restarted in the early 18th century.

REBELS The hard, dangerous, independent work of a miner could only be performed by those strong both in body and spirit. The royal mine attracted free people not used to bending their necks. No wonder then that right from the beginning rebellions, strikes and protests broke out there. Traces of the first such disturbances can be seen already in the Casimir the Great statute issued in 1368.

The commonest cause of worker unrest were matters of wages. All the categories of diggers and the all-important bearers were paid piece rates; the unqualified hauling employees and the mine apprentices were paid by the day or by the week. The differing working conditions were responsible for the fact that fixing the piece rates was not an easy thing to do and often gave rise to conflicts. The royal administration tried — it has to be handed to them — to create a just system for assessing the miners' work, which, for example, in the case of the gallery-tunnellers had as many as seven different rates depending on the kind and hardness of the geological strata in which they had to tunnel. The bearers were paid on the basis of shifting a specified weight 20 paces. The number of such 20-pace units that each of the hauling routes contained was established by a commission; it considered the rising and sloping of the galleries, uneven floors, bends, narrow or dangerous places, etc. Progress in deposit-exploitation lengthened the hauling routes and made it necessary to keep updating the hauling workers' wages. Another source of animosities between workers and administration were the salt allowances, already referred to on several occasions. The mine master aimed at replacing the salt allowances with money (to be able to control the market) while the miners drew considerable incomes from these, their value at time exceeding their basic wages.

Rebellions and strikes about work safety also broke out. The lease-holders "made economies" in protecting the headings, while the workers refused to work in places likely to cave in. It has to be added that cases of sabotage were very rare; the workers' petitions and protests refer to the salt mine as "our mounts", "the work of our hands", etc. Cases are known of a strike being interrupted in the face of a danger to the mine and of heroic and selfless fight against a fire or water flooding the headings.

The most restive employee groups were always the bearers. This was due (apart from their relatively low wages) to the nature of their work calling for group effort. The need for cooperation and co-responsibility for the results of their work gave rise to a sense of solidarity and also favoured conspiracy.

The strikes and rebellions intensified markedly during the 1580—1690 period. For more than 100 years the mine was aboil; strikes broke out almost every year; in Wieliczka and in Bochnia assemblies were prohibited and ringleaders faced capital punishment and confiscation of property. Violent incidents took place in Bochnia in 1584 when armed miners attacked the mine master's house. The mine master himself, the already mentioned Sebastian Lubomirski, fled for his life through a window.

The riots about the salt allowances were widespread in the Lubomirskis' "Kunegunda" on lease from the royal mines at the time (1679). It all started with a four-week strike; on the arrest of the leaders fighting broke out and they were retaken by their mates. When a few days later the ringleaders were re-captured and a court about to be held, four hundred miners with pickaxes

58

hidden under their clothes surged onto the mine courtyard and forcibly released the captured workers from the officials' hands.

There was a tragic end to the 1690 riots in Wieliczka. The then mine masters Wawrzyniec Wodzicki and Andrzej Kotowski refused the miners their right to salt allowances. A strike broke out. The mine masters called out royal troops but these, recognizing the diggers to be in the right, refused to move in. Attempts were made to break the rebellion by sending strike breakers but the miners chased them from the mine and two of them, Marcin Olszewski and Jan Granat, were beaten to death. When at long last the disturbances were put down, reprisals were atrocious. Four of the ringleaders, the bearers Jan Ceruła, Daniel Dupak, Szymon Lipka and Marcin Bogda, were sentenced to impalement and six others to decapitation and quartering. Eight particularly active "rebels" were also sentenced to death. For her participation in the disturbances Jadwiga Mistaczka was sentenced to be beheaded and four other women were whipped at the pillory. "The others received an amnesty on condition that in two weeks' time they return to work." It is interesting though unexplained that women had taken part in the strike since they were never employed in the mine. Also a mention has been preserved that some part in the miners' strike was played by students at Cracow University.

The Wieliczka diggers also participated in the Poles' national-liberation struggle. In the early 19th century a clandestine independence organization was set up here by the son of the salt-mine physician, Dyzma Chromy. On 24 February 1846 Edward Dembowski read out to the inhabitants of Wieliczka the National Government's manifesto and set off to Cracow at the head of a detail of armed miners. After nine days the "Cracow revolution" fell.

Even the longest years of work down the mine cannot change the fact that the dark, rugged world of the underground galleries is for man an ambience strange, dangerous, mysterious and incomprehensible. The faint flame of an oil lamp casts eerie shadows onto walls sculptured in all sorts of shapes. You can hear the tapping of drops of water falling from somewhere, the crackling and creaking of wooden props and cribs sagging under the pressure of millions of tonnes of earth. From a grey wall a light will suddenly shimmer, reflected from the gleaming surface of a crystal and a rust-coloured salt drop-formation will glint with fresh blood. Human senses wish to identify these eery impressions with sounds and shapes familiar to them above ground. Into events caused by inanimate forces of nature man is anxious to read ordinary human intentions, emotions, feelings. Thus is born a rich world of figures and creatures which exist — although they are not there...

The seven hundred years of the Wieliczka mine's uninterrupted activity has created an excellent breeding ground for numerous legends and myths. A considerable section of today's staff come from families linked with the mine for generations. They have no need to create a mythical world — they simply find underground its mysterious signs and signals that father, grandfather and neighbours have been telling them about.

The Wieliczka apparitions were recorded for the first time in literature by Jodok Willich in 1543: "Down the Wieliczka mine there sometimes come apparitions but only when some misfortune is about to happen that God forbid! These apparitions... assume so diverse shapes that you might say it is a cat, a pig, a man or another sort of animate being running incessantly about. I recollect that there is some sort of earth demon... which not always and not everywhere is harmful and which, indeed — as in certain ore mines — provides

HE AND THE WHITE LADY

59

a stimulus to work and collects output into special baskets. So also here, with its warning, it demands that man should be more prudent and take greater care to ward off an approaching hazard. Let everybody, however, remember a certain old proverb which neither Pliny ever forget: The apparitions' active forces are subject to our control, and as you react to them such power they have."

The last sentence echoes a note of scepticism, typical of a Renaissance humanist. Today's smart alecs are the young engineers who come to the mine with a fresh diploma from an institution of higher education and confidence in present-day science. So burdened, they stop in an underground gallery in front an air-dam door which refuses to open and they can go on for an hour about the circulation of air in the mine, about over- and underpressure, etc. Even the longest lectures, however, can do nothing to change the situation: the door stays closed. It is not until an old miner comes up to it and asks: "Let go!" that HE stops holding it on the other side and you can go ahead. If he happens to lose his way in the maze of old headings the young engineer begins nervously to analyze the situation. An experienced man quietly sits down for a while and asks, "Don't lead me astray." HE is understanding; as long as HE has no special reason HE does not harm the men, although HE can play a prank on them. After such a plea the miner looks round and, suddenly, he recognizes a familiar place.

HE is as old as the mine or as the salt in the Wieliczka ground. Today the tourist book-guides often describe Him as Skarbnik (the Treasurer). In olden times people were scared of saying His name and they simply would say: HE. Most often HE appears as an old, tall, keen-sighted foremen. His lamp gives an unnatural, bright light. HE can be everywhere; policing order in the mine he penetrates walls, turns up in places inaccessible to man, with a motion of the hand HE brings down huge chambers, or tunnels wide galleries in the body of salt. HE is the conscience of the mining community: He cannot stand laziness, dishonesty, arrogance, conceit, HE is irritated by shouting and whistling down the mine. HE has his foibles — surely due to His advanced age; in various parts of the Wieliczka deposit he hides, e.g. provisions: some cones, seeds, a leaf impression. HE can generously reward conscientiousness, honesty, industry. HE does not have to appear in person to do so. It is enough for Him to warn of an imminent cave-in with small salt lumps falling from the ceiling.

Meetings with HIM are still much talked about in Wieliczka today. Here are two excerpts from the many stories recorded by ethnographers a few years ago:

"My father would tell me that he had often seen Him, this light. Once, as they went to work, it obstructed their way. They wanted to go round it but

no. It kept obstructing their way. They tried another way and it went on coming at them. One of them said: 'Don't let's go to work, something might happen'. And they didn't. And later on that day the hole they had been working in caved in and a horse and two men were killed."

"In olden times when a miner got his wages he immediately gave something to beggars so as not to anger the Treasurer with his meanness. Once there was a German foreman who would never give anybody anything. The Treasurer met him in the 'Mayer' chamber where the foreman had gone to take a rest. He slapped him on the snout and said: 'I'll let you have more of that for the wrongs you've done, you're not going to earn anything'. That foreman was then sacked for drunkennes and so the Treasurer's words had come true."

An unusual apparition — not met anywhere else in the miners' mythology — is the figure of Bieliczka or the White Lady, a beautiful, white-clad woman. At first there was no knowing where she had come to the mine from. It was not until the genesis of the Wieliczka deposits was known that the riddle was solved: it was the daughter of the king of the sea that used to roar here, imprisoned for ever in salt after the waters had dried up. Bieliczka has a typically feminine character: she leads astray a miner spellbound by her charm in order to ruin him. She usually tries to get him to get round some mining regulations; she may ask to be guided along a gallery closed due to a possible cave-in, for a lamp to be lit where this threatens a methane explosion, etc. At times she pretends to be very tired or to have a sore foot and entreats him to take her up to the surface. In a dangerous spot she then turns into a heavy salt block and crushes the miner. Unlike the stern but just Treasurer she is the personification of perversity, falsehood and evil.

Apart from Treasurer, Bieliczka, the devils and frights you can come on the souls of the miners who have died here underground: "A miner was buried during the period of Austrian rule somewhere at the third level. He had gone there without anybody knowing and it was not until the next day that they saw a cave-in near the place they had been working. There was no moving the cave-in and the man remained there. After some time the miners began saying that a light was walking about the place all by itself. They were scared of passing there and said that it was the soul of the buried man. Once, as they sat near that cave-in because they had been working nearby, they saw that light as it was writing a cross and date on the wall with lampblack. They at once put up a little wooden cross there and wrote the date of the accident and then they paid for mass and prayed every day for their mate's soul. Then after some time when they had not been working there they came to that cave-in and saw, written up on the wall with lampblack "May Heaven reward you."

That story, recounted by a 56-year-old miner, explains the origin of the many shrines, pictures or just the crosses hewn in the salt side walls. The biggest shrines were put up by the mine and served as a place for collective prayers. The crosses and the holy pictures were also hung by workers on their own in chambers they were currently working and they often took them along to their new workplaces. The first mention in the mine's records comes from 1518 and refers to the shrine in the "Boczaniec" chamber, the place where a fire broke out in 1696. Thanks to the scrupulosity of the royal commissioners we have a detailed description of it today: "The wooden shrine which had a partition made... of sawn timber. In that partition were two glass windows to give light to the worker when candles or lamps were alight in the shrine; the door to that shrine was similiter made of sawn timber. On entering it there were wooden banisters round the altar, and the altar, made of wood, stood by the side of a small crib; on the altar stood a big, wooden figure of the Passion, nailed to the same small crib; by the figure were four paper angels; a table, as is usual in front of an altar, was always covered with a cloth and on it — for decoration — stood various paper flowers as well as candles in wooden candlesticks which were always lighted for singing the litanies. Paper pictures were glued to its sides."

Christ, the Virgin Mary, the Blessed Kinga, the Guardian Angel, St. Barbara, St. Anthony, St. Clement — all were supposed to protect men from danger, from the White Lady, from cave-ins and mishaps. Their presence made it possible to replace the horrific mechanism of blind chance with comprehensible regulations of reward for good and punishment for evil. The most convincing evidence of the Wieliczka miners' religious feelings are inscriptions in underground galleries. In the 19th century the Austrians brought into the mine wooden plates bearing chamber-names and pointing to emergency ways to the shaft, etc. On one such plate an awkward hand wrote with a pencil this couplet:

"God is of help to him
Who calls to him for help".

Somebody's thanks for finding his way in the dark labyrinth? Somebody's call for help in an emergency?...

From the time of the fire in the "Boczaniec," shrines were sculptured in salt walls. The oldest one of this type well preserved to this day is the St. Anthony shrine, dedicated a bare two years after the fire. The altars and bas-reliefs have been hewn in the body of salt and the free-standing monument in separate salt blocks.

The best-known and biggest is the chapel — or, indeed, church — of the Blessed Kinga. It was hewn in the inside of a green-salt block which was being worked in the years 1852—88 as the "Panzenberger" chamber (after the name of the Austrian court councillor). Work on transforming the mining heading into a chapel was begun in 1895, under the leadership of Józef Markowski. He was helped in his work by his brother and a group of some 20 miners. Markowski's work was continued right down to 1963 by Antoni Wyrodek.

MINING FAMILIES   His family comes from Marków Wielki in Podlasie. The fortunes of war brought Jan Markowski, a marshal of the Bar confederacy in Volhynia, to Wieliczka. Soon the parish records featured the names of his widow, Marianna née Głogowska, and of his son Kazimierz. There is no trace of Jan — he probably died here and was buried nameless to avoid reprisals. His son soon took up a job as a cart-driver in the mine. All the generations of the Markowski family have worked here ever since.

The author of the Blessed Kinga chapel, Józef, was born in 1860. Having sculpted in wood since he was 16, he tried to sculpt in salt on beginning work down the mine. That drew the attention of Edward Windakiewicz, an engineer who suggested to young Markowski the renovation of the sculptures in the old chapels. In 1895 it was decided on Windakiewicz's initiative to set up underground a new chapel dedicated to the Blessed Kinga. The main work was entrusted to Józef Markowski, who, after 22 years of work as a cart-driver, was made a bearer.

Markowski's education was restricted to six weeks of instruction in writing and reading by an old Siercza farmer, Mateusz. He made designs for the bas-reliefs in the Blessed Kinga chapel from illustrations in popular religious publications. He first drew sketches on paper and with the mine board's approval he drew them in outline onto a side walls in charcoal. He made the charcoal himself — he singed over a miner's oil lamp staves of broken barrels of which the headings were full. He sculpted with tools that were used by the miners in hewing salt blocks; only in modelling the details he used a razor. During his 25 years' work on the chapel he drew the same wages as his mates working on the deposit.

Markowski's skill was known to his neighbours and friends. At the request of Wieliczka engineers he sculpted figures of saints for them. In 1901 the Siercza commune commissioned him to make a wayside Pietà. His wife sitting in a chair and his 14-year-old son, Franciszek, lying at her feet posed for him. His father sculpted the boy naked; to his mother's protests about the "scandal" he replied that "you cannot do a body from your head". His Pietà, which broke with the canons of inconography, drew objections from the inhabitants of Siercza. To the query of why Christ was not lying on the Virgin Mary's knees only resting at her feet, Markowski would reply: "How could an emaciated Virgin Mary hold her 30-year-old son on her knees?"

In his work on the chapel Józef was helped by his brother Tomasz who later took to souvenir-making. He was a man talented not only in sculpting: he also designed and built a house of his own, he made locks and mended clocks.

The sixth Markowski generation is represented today by Ignacy, Tomasz's grandson and the present managing director of the mine. He used to paint in his youth and now has no time to do so; he only appears in the "Lutnia" amateur choir established in 1872.

The Markowskis are not an exception in Wieliczka for multigenerational links with the mine and for artistic tastes, which is expressed by, among other things, their pursuit of an art unknown anywhere else: salt sculpting.

An unusual chapter in the mine's history has been written by the Morsztyn family of landed gentry. The first of them, Jerzy, became a Wieliczka salt-panning master in the early 15th century: from that time on till the end of independent Poland this office was to be held exclusively by the Morsztyns. Let us add that theirs was not a hereditary post: each Morsztyn received a separate royal appointment. This family's traditions were respected even by the Austrians who abolished all the appointments and rents guaranteed by privileges from Polish kings: the Emperor Josef II in 1774 granted — exceptionally — a lifelong pension to Jan Kanty Morsztyn in recognition of his ancestors' services to the Wieliczka mine. The Morsztyns are an absolute exception in the history of the Polish landed gentry — there is no other family to have had such consistent connections with industrial activities. The excellence and splendour of this family is recalled today by the 17th-century, baroque Morsztyn chapel in the parish church, adorned with Balthasar Fontana stuccos.

Another family fairly typical of the Cracow salt mines was the Kuczkiewicz family. Michał, in 1772, assumed the function of tallow man in Bochnia. He worked for 51 years in the mine ending his career as head of the salt storehouse. His son, Karol, began work earlier still — when he was 15 years old. He then completed studies at the Academy of Mining and Forestry in Banská Štiavnica in Slovakia (where he met Józef Russegger, the later director of the Wieliczka mine whom we shall refer to later) and returned to his native parts to hold a number of functions — right up to mine manager — in Wieliczka and in Bochnia. Karol's son Emil also worked in the mines but poor health did not allow him to make a career in the hierarchy of salt-mine clerks, while Emil's son Stanisław reached the highest dignities of the four Kuczkiewicz genera-

tions: in 1905 he became head of all salt mining in Galicia. It is to him that the salt mines owe the organization of a permanent rescue service, a social-welfare system as well as an orderly pay rates table and promotion rules. Thanks to Stanisław Kuczkiewicz, Bochnia and Wieliczka had water piping put in. Today one of the Wieliczka streets, a working level and a chamber in the mine are named after Kuczkiewicz.

The period from the end of the 18th century to the beginning of the 20th century in Wieliczka abounded in fine figures of the contemporary "technical intelligentsia". Those miner-engineers were not only high-class specialists in their field. For the most part they had a thorough humanist education which made them see in their work place more than just production and technological-progress indices. They took a lively interest in history; they collected and published materials which today make a valuable source for studies of Wieliczka's history. They were ardent patriots: with Poland erased from the political map of Europe they considered it their duty to popularize the Cracow mines not only as a *lusus naturae* or a museum of mining technology but first of all as a monument to the Poles' work. Their names can be seen both on the covers of scientific theses and in popular periodicals, brochures or guide-books. At the turn of the 19th and the 20th century the community of the Polish intelligentsia put on a number of campaigns to stimulate national consciousness and spread education among the miners. There were the Popular Reading Room, the Popular School Society, the Miners' Reading Room, and the already-mentioned "Lutnia" Choral Society, the "Sokół" Gymnastics Society, and from 1912, the Riflemen's Union. The mining school held a series of public lectures on hygiene, child-rearing, fighting alcoholism, etc.

A great work like the Blessed Kinga chapel would also have been impossible had it not been for the encouragement, help and protection of the mine board. Apart from the Edward Windakiewicz, the initiator of the chapel project and Józef Markowski's patron, great services were rendered here by Erazm Barącz and Feliks Piestrak. The former, a surveyor, a working-field manager and the mine director, was at the same time an art collector, studied painting and mingled with Cracow's artists. The latter, also a mining engineer, at first worked in the mine and later become headmaster of the State Mining School in Wieliczka. He is the author of a great number of scientific contributions and popular works (including a guide-book) about the history of the Wieliczka salt mine.

Wieliczka has a way with arrivals from foreign parts. This thesis was amply confirmed in the 18th and 19th centuries when the first Saxons came over here followed by representatives of the constituent nations of the Austrian monarchy. In this mass of clerks come to administer a conquered country, Wieliczka aroused admiration and respect as a monument to the work and capabilities of the Polish nation. It was with true passion that many of them started to tackle the problems of the old mine. There have also been those who became integrated into the Polish community and stayed here for good.

Priority among the arrivals must, however, go to someone who is a little familiar to us already: Marcin German. We do not know too much about him, some historians even doubting his Swedish origin. In Wieliczka he held the post of foreman of the "Regis" mount for many long years, drew up rules for calculating workers' wages and made the first charts of the mine. He completed those charts in 1638; seven years later they were printed by Wilhelm Hondius, a Dutch copper engraver, the court artist to Kings Ladislaus IV and John Casimir. In the Hondius edition vignettes depicting the work of the salt-panning works and of the mine were added to the Wieliczka foremen's work. The engraver must have gone by some German drawings unknown to us today since his engravings show a perfect knowledge of the principles of deposit working, output hauling, crib building, etc. In the European iconography the Hondius vignettes can be compared only with the illustrations almost a hundred years earlier to Georgius Agricola's work *De re metallica*, presenting methods of winning and processing metal ores. From such a comparison, we might add, Hondius emerges victorious both for faithfulness of presentation of miners' work and for the artistic standard of the drawings.

By a strange coincidence another of the foreigners to have rendered services to Wieliczka was also the author of complete mine charts and a talented artist in drawing. This time, however, his sketches presenting the Wieliczka miners' work had been put together on a single large-scale illustration and brought out separately even earlier than the charts (in 1766 by J. E. Nilson in Augsburg). We are referring to Johann Gottfried Borlach.

He was the son of a Dresden joiner and born in 1687. His uncommon abilities drew the attention of Saxony's rulers thanks to whom he gained an education in the fields of chemistry, painting, geology and mechanics. He turned up in Wieliczka in 1717 as a mine surveyor, was quickly promoted and in 1743 assumed the management of the whole enterprise. Borlach carried out a veritable revolution in the salt mines in the field of haulage. He lengthened the day shafts below the first level, organized a system for lowering output onto the main hauling levels using braking gear, provided the treadmills with brakes and set up the mine's rope-making workshops. He attached great importance to securing the headings, prohibited further exploitation of the first level and vigorously set about drawing off water using for the first time handworked pendulum pumps. He was an able organizer and drew up a new wages table, raising the wages and doing away with the salt allowances — the perennial source of conflict between staff and administrators. It is also to him that Wieliczka owes the detailed fire regulations quoted above.

Borlach produced several first-rate surveyors who, on his departure from the salt mines, supplemented and published the mine charts he had made. One of them was Jan Stolarski, whose father Antoni had died tragically during the Bochnia mine fire in 1745. In an effort to get through to the place of the fire, Antoni Stolarski, accompanied by a candler, began to go down the "Zaporów" shaft. At the time those going down communicated with the treadmill minder by means of a string hanging loose in the shaft and attached to a bell at the surface. Smoke having enveloped Stolarski, he tugged at the string once (for "stop") and then he meant to be pulled up (three peals of the bell). However, he pulled at the string only twice (for "down") because he had fainted. The treadmill minder kept lowering the rope for some time and it was not until further signals had failed to come and because of the smoke issuing from the shaft, that he pulled them up. The candler was dead while Antoni Stolarski died two months later. The orphaned Jan's upbringing was taken over by Johann Gottfried Borlach, manager of the salt mines at the time.

In 1750 Borlach left Wieliczka and returned to his native Saxony. He worked in the local salines for a time and also made a number of technical improvements in the textile industry. He died in 1768.

Other newcomers of service to Wieliczka were the Hrdin brothers. Jan Nepomucen proved equal to the task of draining waters gathered in the worked-out chambers by means of a patent of his own: the now familiar to us method of drilling holes and stopping them with a wooden tapped bung. He was the author of an extensive and valuable history of the mine. He did not manage to publish the book as he died in Wieliczka during the typhoid epidemic in 1831. The *Geschichte der Wieliczkaer Saline* was not brought out until 1842, in Vienna, by the author's brother Ludwik Emanuel who provided it with a series of 12 drawings presenting the mine's interior. Jan Nepomucen and Ludwik Emanuel worked in the mine as surveyors; the third of the brothers, Alojzy, was the builder of the "Turówka" salt-works which never went into production.

Another foreigner, Josef Russegger, stayed in Wieliczka for a very short time — a mere two years (1846—48) — holding the post of mine director. This character is worth recalling because of his interesting life story and his eminent scientific standing in the field of mining and geology. A graduate from the Academy of Mining and Forestry in Banská Štiavnica, he managed the salines in Salzburg and the gold mines in Böckstein. In the years 1835—38 he managed prospecting for ore and coal deposits in Egypt, Sudan, Palestine, Lebanon and Syria. After a spell as head of Wieliczka he became director of the Banská Štiavnica Academy. Towards his subordinates he was very demanding but just and human; after the fall of the Kossuth uprising in Hungary he saved the Academy's clerks who had taken part in it from reprisals.

To Russegger Wieliczka owes numerous palaeontological discoveries; he took a lively interest in the organic remains occuring in the deposit and gathered together a whole collection of them (which later found its way to Vienna). Palaeontological specimens had been found in the Wieliczka mine for a long time, the first mention about them having been by Ulysses Aldrovandi in his work *Musaeum Metallicum* in 1648.

In the 17th century the miners made queen Marie Louise, the wife of John Casimir, a present of a salt lump with a "birch twig complete with leaves" embedded inside. Similar specimens must have been uncovered more often as in the 1743 regulations Borlach orders the exploratory-shaft sinkers: "Whenever salt shows in their work or they find such other more peculiar things as mussels as well as coals and other novelties of any sort... they should show them to their foremen and report."

TOURIST ATTRACTIONS

We have so far been dealing with people linked with the mine permanently — people of big business or back-breaking work — but always insiders of the Polish salt. How has Wieliczka been perceived by those who have come over here as visitors? What has it been in the collective consciousness of Polish society?

The mine had its first invasion in the 16th century during the Renaissance-time fascination with the riches and variety of the world. Travels at the time

were an indispensable supplement to one's education. This peculiar notion of tourism later yielded descriptions of lands visited or other works of differing value.

The first such work wholly devoted to the Wieliczka mine was by the eminent German humanist Conradus Celtes. He stayed in Poland in the years 1488—90 and exerted a great influence on contemporary cultural life in the country. It is probably on his information that the reference to Wieliczka is based in Hartmann Schedel's *Chronicon mundi*, published in Nuremberg in 1493. Then the Cracow salt mines were described by Joachim Vadian, Jodok Willich and Adam Schroeter. Other accounts are contained in the reports by papal nuncios: Bernardo Bongiovanni (he visited Poland in 1560) and Fulvius Ruggieri (1565). A description of Wieliczka was also carried in his memoirs by Jean Choisnin who accompanied the French envoy Jean Balagni on his trip to Poland before the election of Henry de Valois in 1572. He wrote that the mine is "an underground place which it takes half an hour to lower yourself into by means of big and strong ropes that can carry the weight of fifty persons going down at a time... Underground, we saw huge caves hewn in salt rock rather like streets in a town". Three years later Wieliczka was visited by the Venetian envoy Girolamo Lippomano: "The depth of the mine itself is equal to the height of the St. Mark belfry. It is illuminated by torch light and one can cover five miles along its caves, of which some are as high and roomy as our Great Council hall." Towards the end of the century, in 1597, the mine was visited by Jakub Esprinchard, who, having completed his legal studies in Leiden, was on a European tour meant to improve his education. It was him who attributed to the Wieliczka miners a character as glorious as it was deceptive: "We have seen in the innards of the earth more than five hundred peasants who, stark naked, work in the mines, each with a flaming lamp, and most of them speak very good Latin."

The Latin-speaking miners are, however, nothing much in comparison with the revelations of Laboureur, a Frenchman in the retinue of Madame de Guebriant who arrived in Poland in 1646 with Maria Louise Gonzaga, the second wife of Ladislaus IV. He begins his story with a very flattering for us and often-quoted statement: "Two miles from Cracow lie Wieliczka's salt mines no less exquisite then the Egyptian pyramids, only more useful. For they make a commendable memento of the Poles' industry while the latter are proof of the Egyptians' tyranny and vanity." We soon learn, however, how terrifying going down the shaft was, and that "the danger of the ropes quenches in many a person their curiosity of lowering themselves down that mine; I, too, was not allowed to do that by the Polish Landed Gentleman, a good friend of mine". But Laboureur does not let down his reader's expectations: like present-day journalists he determines to gain — at all cost — information about what the mine looks like. "Two gentlemen from our party, Messrs d'Incarville and de Briscoli have been there and assured us that one can lower oneself close on three miles down those strings, excepting a ladder with two hundred or three hundred spokes; that more than five hundred families live down that precipice, that they have hewn for themselves in that salt bedrock something like a town complete with streets and comfortable accommodation; that there are children down there who have never left there and who have no idea of another world. They have also seen churches, priests, a judge and other officials; marriages are contracted there and babies are often born. The whole diversion of those underground inhabitants consists in hewing that rock salt that Poles, Silesians, Moravians, Austrians and Germans buy."

That is how the fright of an emotion-laden trip down a rope gave rise to myths which later did the rounds of Europe and added to the fame of the Wieliczka salt mines. The Laboureur story was still quoted in 1789 in *Le grand dictionnaire géographique et critique* by Bruzen la Martinière who appended this apt observation: "Travellers' accounts usually allow of some fabrications to compensate the readers for what the author considers unnecessary and boring."

The only account of a going down the mine without fear and, indeed, with gusto has been penned by... a woman: the novelist Klementyna Hoffmanowa née Tańska, who visited Wieliczka in 1827. At first she may have felt not too secure: "We came to the mine's orifice, a place that looks like a shed; inside is an orifice shaped like a huge well and down it go workers and the curious; a glimpse at this dark abyss down which you're supposed to go sends an involuntary chill down your spine, the pen you're passed to enter your name with in the special book trembles lightly in your hand and the long linen shirts that the trippers are clad with to protect their clothes seem to resemble the last death garb." When, however, the novelist had taken a winch seat and the treadmill begun to turn... "Indescribable is the pleasant feeling during this trip; there is something ideal in it, a resemblance of those pleasant dreams of us ploughing the air in a fast and single flight. Not one fearful thought occurs to you, you're just sorry to feel the speed slow down, see ground close by, and to have to get off." Well, the old Polish proverb says "where the devil cannot go, he sends a woman..."

Together with the popular authoress we have moved to the 19th century — another epoch of increased popularity for Wieliczka. This is largely owed to the Austrians who, appreciating the scenic and cognitive values of the mine, advertised it as one of the most magnificent "tourist" attractions of the monarchy. Still in the 18th century soon after Wieliczka was taken, a few historic chambers at the first level were made accessible to visitors, and thus the head of the present-day tourist route was laid out. One by one, more interiors came to be included in it, also at the second and third levels, adding to it a number of attractions that brought out the charm of the underground rooms and added to the pleasure of visiting. The route was splendidly-illuminated; in the "Michalowice" chamber, for example, there hung a huge chandelier (5.5 m. high, close on 3 m. across) made of salt crystals, and lit up with 300 candles. To lit it, an old treadmill installed in the overlying "Urszula" chamber was used. Visitors were accompanied by torch-holding miners, fireworks were displayed, and the more spectacular fragments of the almost five-kilometre route were illuminated. The attractions included passing "over the bridge across the precipice", a boat trip across a saline-water lake, a show of "dare-devil stunts" by miners lowered down a rope, and listening to the thundering echo of a pistol shot. The chambers and galleries had salt-hewn obelisks, pillars, monuments, plaques, decorative portals dedicated to various members of the imperial family and to Austrian dignitaries. In the "Łętów" chamber, converted into a ballroom, you could dance to the strains of a miners' band or see a show of the "Cracow wedding". In the late 19th century another attraction was added — a 2.5-km.-long ride in horse-drawn bedecked waggons. From 1774 visitors' names were entered in a special book. These include the names of Tsar Alexander I, the Emperor Francis I, Johann Wolfgang Goethe, Alexander Humboldt, Frédéric Chopin, Jan Matejko, Dimitr Mendeleev, Sarah Bernhardt, Bolesław Prus, Henryk Sienkiewicz, the Rev. Angelo G. Roncalli (the later Pope John XXIII), the Rev. Karol Wojtyła (John Paul II) and many, many others.

The Austrians' popularization campaign proved successful; the old mine became famous in Europe. So much so that an English geography handbook from the end of the 19th century after an extensive description of Wieliczka carried a brief mention that not far from the mine was Cracow, the old coronation city of the Polish kings. The mention — apart from the grotesque disproportions between Wieliczka and Cracow — is also important in that it is impossible to mention the Wieliczka underground without adding that it is proof of the magnificent power of a state that was absent from the contemporary maps of Europe.

For Poles in all the three partition zones Wieliczka was the destination of patriotic pilgrimages, a place in which despite the Austrian props you could "breathe Polishness a little". The Krzyżanowski book firm, which made a notable contribution to national culture, held "rallies to the salines" every year at Whitsuntide. This is how Marian Krzyżanowski recalls them: "Those rallies were attended by Poles from all the partition zones but the most numerous were workers employed in Germany, in the Westphalia mines and industry. They then breathed a romantic national atmosphere, went down the mine by torchlight, and listened to the guides' stories, stories linked to the salines' history and the national legend. They took with them lumps of Polish salt as relics and bought various artistic products made of salt for those who had been unable to come along."

Especially warm feelings went to Wieliczka at the time from the propagators of positivism who saw the nation's future in economic and cultural development of the Polish lands. The mine was for them an excellent example of the glorious industrial and technical traditions.

In the years 1826—46, yet another claim to fame for Wieliczka was the local spa. The curative properties of salt had been described by many ancient writers. Their theses were recalled by the humanists who visited the mine in the 16th century. Schroeter maintained that sprinkling salt over a wound hastens the healing process. Vadian referred to salt as a laxative and Willich maintained that salt mixed with other substances heals snake and scorpion bites, eczema, pimples, warts, ulcers, bloodshot eyes, bruises, caries, sore throat, gout and venereal diseases into the bargain. In 1562 a doctor called Antoni Schneeberger brought out in Cracow a work entitled *De multiplici salis usu* dedicated to the salt-mine master Hieronim Bużyński and discussing at length the diverse applications of salt in medicine.

Wieliczka's career as a spa stemmed from the 19th-century balneology fad. The many substances that patients were soaked in at the time must include saline solutions. As early as 1826 patients began to flock to the town and rented rooms from landlords offering baths in tubs filled with saline water brought over from the mine. The initiative to build a real spa came from the then mine physician Feliks Boczkowski, the author of the valuable survey *O Wieliczce pod względem historii naturalnej, dziejów i kąpieli* (About Wieliczka in respect of its natural history and baths). The joint-stock company he set up opened a bathing establishment in 1839 which recommended 12 well-appointed rooms in which to take warm baths with salt water, salt mud, potassium polysulphide, and sulphur water from nearby, with malt decoction and finally all sorts of fall and drip baths "by means of a newly-fangled and privileged machine". Subsequent years saw the opening of a "salt and Russian steam bath-house, bath-house for the many" and "four bathrooms for Orthodox Jews". Doctor Boczkowski's plans also included "common baths and sea baths

TREATMENT
OF DISSIPATED

69

with imitation waves". That was the treatment for 36 disease units ranging from the common cold to infertility and from hysteria to "weakening from age, weakening from hard childbirth and serious diseases, weakening from masturbation and excesses in love-making". The fun-lovers must have been many, as over a period of 20 years the Wieliczka spa was visited by more than 3,000. Doctor Boczkowski had the town tidied up, a theatre set up and a park laid out in which a miners' band played for the patients.

The bath-house building was destroyed after the Cracow revolution in 1846. Saline-bath treatment came to a definitive end in 1855 when Feliks Boczkowski died while coming to the aid of the people of Wieliczka during a cholera epidemic. Attempts were later made to revive the town's traditions as a spa but these were thwarted by the two world wars.

The sanatorium was revived in 1958 on the initiative of Professor Mieczysław Skulimowski. He was the first man in the world to have instituted — in the 1960s — scientific research in a new branch of medicine with a somewhat lengthy name: subterraneotherapy. At present respiratory tract diseases, mainly bronchial asthma, chronic bronchitis and allergic catarrh, are treated down the mine. The treatment results bring Wieliczka a well-earned renown among specialist physicians. The specific microclimate, the adequate humidity and air temperature as well as the absence of allergens cause disease symptoms to recede with 60% of the patients at the end of 21 days of treatment for a period between six and twelve months. It has to be added that it is the most serious asthma cases that are referred here — close on three-fourths of the patients are people who have been ill for more than 10 years. Four times a week patients spend five hours on end, and twice a whole night, in three chambers at a depth of 211 metres. The sanatorium can take on 65 patients at a time, which is the proverbial drop in the 500,000-strong ocean of allergics in Poland. Plans were afoot in the 1970s for the construction in Wieliczka of a health-resort hospital with a thousand places and for the conversion of the underground chambers to take on four hundred patients at time. Unfortunately, this conception never got beyond the "wishful thinking" stage. Since the chambers currently used are likely to cave-in, the sanatorium is being moved elsewhere, and the number of places will be increased to a hundred.

Let us hope the long-closed salinary baths will at long last be renovated, which will make it possible to treat allergic skin diseases with saline baths. At present the only continuation of Wieliczka's fine balneological traditions is the production here of the sought-after cosmetic bathing salts.

The view that the Wieliczka salt has curative properties has also been revived (if in a completely changed form). Scientists maintain that the cause of many of the diseases (including tumours) is the absence of the bioelements, or microscopic quantities — assimilated together with our food and water — of magnesium, iodine, cobalt, iron, lithium etc. They are almost entirely absent from the chemically pure sodium chloride that boiled salt is; a wide range of these, on the other hand, is to be found in the Wieliczka rock salt. The eminent scientist and civic activist Prof. Dr Julian Aleksandrowicz of Cracow has for years now been conducting a regular battle to have precisely such natural salt passed fit for consumption. The Wieliczka mine is already turning it out but for the time being the country's sanitary authorities are allowing its use exclusively as an additive to cattle feedstuffs.

So the Wieliczka mine has become famous not only as a *lusus naturae* and a "monument to Polishness" but also as a therapeutic establishment. Its diverse values and standing — unique in the world — have taken the organization of a specialist scientific agency for studies of Wieliczka's history and popularization of the old mine. This function is being performed by the Cracow Salt Mines Museum which owes its existence to Alfons Długosz.

He found his way to Wieliczka at the start of World War II, after having completed painting studies in Berlin and Dresden and worked as a secondary-school teacher for a dozen or so years in various Polish towns. After the liberation he worked as a teacher in Wieliczka. His passion for civic activities soon led him to make his first contacts with the mine's board of directors — Długosz helped arrange all sorts of mining celebrations. Let us listen to what he says:

"As a miners' guest at a Barbórka* laid on in 1949 in the Wieliczka underground I made a close contact with the mine. It was then that, frightened with what I had noticed, I decided to help save a priceless historic relic. I understood that it [the mine] had to be recalled and simply shown to society which had not known and did not know it. For it was not known even by those who come to it everyday because of their occupation. I was aware of what I was letting myself in for. I had no funds, all my capital consisting of my own hands and a lot of good intentions. All I could expect from the mine board was just some irregular help. I set to work vigorously, though. I looked for an experienced miner among the staff who knew the mine's labyrinth, had a keen mind, and above all an affection for mining traditions. I found one in the person of the dedicated miner Franciszek Krzeczkowski, who, employed in the surveying section for tens of years, had on many occasions tramped the old galleries and chambers and, led by an intuitive curiosity and a wish to know, he penetrated the most out-of-the-way nooks. He got to know the old mine like his own home and he loved it with all his heart. Now he made me an excellent and invaluable companion in my searches.

"By common effort, from the underground labyrinth of the falls, abysses and old carcasses we tore ancient discarded or forgotten work tools, quaint machines and installations of centuries before. We eagerly gathered them together in an underground chamber. They were meant to prove the enormity of the miners' centuries-long toil and to document the thousand-year-long history — marked with streams of sweat and blood — of the people of an underground land. We collected rocks and salts, fossils and crystals and stashed them away so they could bespeak the riches of our native land. I filled chamber after chamber with those treasures."

His long and often dangerous wanderings in the mine's old nooks and crannies were pure pleasure compared with the obstacles that awaited Długosz above ground. The mining authorities of a young state looked at the Wieliczka mine exclusively from the point of view of economic indices and usefulness. These cannot have amounted to much since in 1949 it was intended to lixiviate the remaining salt out of the chambers and shut down the enterprise. Alfons Długosz began a struggle to save the old headings. Thanks to his perseverance, dedication and thanks to his way with people, he won. He was able to convince the then "higher ups" that apart from the volume of salt production there were other, at least just as precious, values. And then he started on another battle. This time to set up a museum.

The Poles do not hold their record of achievement in the field of civilization, technology, and industry in much respect. The fortunes of this corner of Europe

---

* St. Barbara's Day (4 December) is the traditional miners' festival — translator's note.

have been such that at all times the sabre, the rifle or a song rousing to battle have meant more than river regulation, road-making or steel production. To this day many of the visitors perceive the Wieliczka underground more as a *lusus naturae* or a "national temple" than the inside of the country's oldest industrial enterprise. No wonder then that a few tens of years ago the idea of making the old, wooden machines into museum exhibits drew a none too enthusiastic reaction. Had Długosz demanded the construction of a modern, glazed pavilion above ground, well... but a museum underground?

Długosz pulled through, though. In 1951 he opened the first small exhibition in the "Warszawa" chamber. Ten years later an independent institution under the Ministry of Culture and Arts — the Cracow Salt Mines Museum — came into being. It began to extend fast including more and more chambers at the third mine level and attracting — just as the tourist route under the mine's board — great numbers of visitors. Unfortunately, the walls bearing traces of the old-time miners' work on the tourist routes have been effectively obstructed with monuments to persons worthy of respect but having little to do with mining. Hence many a participant in a school excursion today leaves the "Daniłowicz" shaft convinced that Wieliczka was dug by Nicolaus Copernicus jointly with General Świerczewski with the help of the "Brotherhood-in-arms" and the gnomes from the "Gnomes' Chamber"...

Długosz was no outstanding painter; his paintings gracing the Museum rooms do very well as a teaching aid (they present particular stages of work down the mine) but they can hardly be counted among masterpieces of Euro pean art. His scientific activity is also largely objectionable today and needs some considerable correcting. But he was an excellent popularizer and a fine man. He rallied around himself a group of young researchers onto whom his passion — the old mine — rubbed off. He could generate a truly family atmosphere that is fondly remembered by the Professor's disciples to this day. It is thanks to this that within a relatively short time the Museum's young team carried out wide-flung and multifaceted studies on the history of the Cracow salt mines, studies that called for much more work that could be expected from their formal contracts and measly salaries.

Let us quote the Professor once again. He ended the introduction to his book *Wieliczka — Magnum Sal* with these words: "Call on all those who will read this book to remember that Wieliczka is a priceless gem that has no equal in the world and on which the gaze of the world is fixed. Wieliczka is the cradle and school of Polish mining. As the work of forty Polish mining generations, Wieliczka is spellbinding proof of the antiquity and greatness of a native culture.

"Wieliczka is like Poland's heart which ever since the nation's beginning has been incessantly beating the rhythm of intensive work inside our native soil. Historical disasters, war conflagrations, centuries of foreign domination have been unable to stop this pulse, this hard rhythm of work by the peasant from the Polish land in the Polish salt."

Prospects

The difference between Wieliczka and all other historic monuments lies, among other things, in the fact that in the field of conserving works of architecture and the arts there exist ready-made, devised and tested methods. A way for saving salt mines is yet to be invented as there has been no need for one, all having collapsed before time had managed to give them historical value in human eyes. Attempts undertaken recently (for purely economic considerations) in France and the Federal Republic of Germany to prolong the working of present-day mines of this type have ended in a failure — about 10 mines have had to be flooded since there was no stopping the process of deposit lixiviation by water.

Scientific expertises say that should Wieliczka be left to fend for itself today and the natural processes of deposit compression not interfered with, then at the end of 160 years the mine would have ceased to exist. Of course, this is a purely theoretical statement since in practice a catastrophe would have to happen much earlier — as a result of flooding, deposit-lixiviation by water, etc. In any case, however you reckon it, the result will be the same: we have not got much time left.

The first of Wieliczka's problems stems from an atypical deposit structure. We must recall its geological structure: the mine's upper levels are blocks of hard green salt — hollowed from the inside — in a way "floating" in soft loams. Underneath are the headings left after the exploitation of deposit salts, far less resistant to the pressure strata. Many of them, to make things worse, are post-lixiviation chambers, the results of all the salt having been washed out from the deposit. Hence, the top-lying and so the oldest and most valuable headings of the mine today hang over the emptiness of the younger, brittle levels. The laws of physics are inexorable: all this is bound to collapse sometime. The only rescue is by backfilling (i.e. filling the lower levels with sand) thereby making a strong foundation under the mine's oldest levels. The backfilling technology is known and widely applied in mining: sand is mixed with water and pumped through piping to the threatened chambers. In Wieliczka, water has to be replaced with concentrate saline water that will not threaten the strata. So far, so simple; things get complicated once you consider the scale of the process. Out of the 7.5 million cu. m. of the underground emptinesses that go to make up today's mine, some 4.5 million cu. m. would have to be backfilled. Since 1836 when sand backfilling was first applied in Wieliczka, a mere one million cu. m. of chambers likely to cave in have been filled by today (i. e. over some 150 years). In recent years the mine has expanded — to the best of its capabilities — a backfilling line reaching a backfilling capacity of 40,000 cu. m. a year. It is not hard to reckon that at this rate the whole process would take more than 100 years. In practice the problem would have been solved much earlier — with the mine's collapsing. Specialists maintain that the minimal backfilling capacity needed to save Wieliczka should be 100,000—200,000 cu. m. a year, or exactly five times as much. For this target to be reached a large plant must be built on the ground (a pump station, equipment for mixing sand with saline water, etc.) and kilometres of piping put into the mine.

One merit of a programme for backfilling the mine's lower levels is that at least you know how to do it. Worse comes with the water. The only protection can be afforded by putting a preparation in the water-washed-out cracks in the deposit to fill them. Such a preparation must meet three conditions: have the viscosity to go everywhere the saline water does; it must be resistant to its chemical action and be water-impervious. A number of research centres in Poland have been working on inventing such a substance for several years now. Tests are being made with magnesium cements and thixotropic mixtures (i.e. self-setting once at a standstill). Thought is also being given to controlling the crystallization process so that the salt contained in the saline water by itself "closes" the cracks it has washed out. The experiments are yet to bring major results...

Another Wieliczka problem: certain salt grades dry and crack under the influence of air. In many chambers there hang huge crazy slices flaked off from the body of salt. In ore mining what is known as anchoring is applied in such cases: a hole is drilled through the flaked-off slice and the undisturbed soil. It is then filled with a special glue and a metal rod — an anchor tie — is put in. In Wieliczka only the principle has remained of this method. Because of salt's low ability to link with other materials and because of saline water's great chemical activity, brand new glue recipes have had to be devised, and the metal anchor ties replaced with glass-fibre rods. The method is proving itself although it is very labour-intensive: to secure one-third of the ceiling on the tourist route of the "Saurau" chamber more than 400 ties have been used.

Also exceptional but hard-to-solve problems can arise. A few years ago, for example, the backfilling of "Lebzeltern" chambers complex, which were in a very bad repair, began. The pressured headings began to subside because of the "Witos" chambers lying beneath them. And the latter cannot be back filled for the time being since they contain 40 tonnes of slag. The Germans, on taking the mine in 1939, made their work simpler by drilling from the mine's boiler-room on the ground a hole going right down to the "Witos" chambers and dumping slag down there. That went on for a few years after the war. Since the volume of slag shrinks considerably under pressure it is no good as a backfilling material. Attempts have been made to harden slag with substances filling its pores but to no avail because of this material's great chemical activity. All the signs are that this slag — more than 2,600 waggons — will have to be carried out of the "Witos", the chambers filled with sand, and only then will one be able to continue backfilling the "Lebzeltern" complex.

Another need of the Wieliczka mine is air-conditioning. The difference in temperature between the surface and the underground causes the air moisture to condense on the salt walls. This is responsible for the considerable damage to, among other things, the sculptures in the St. Anthony chapel. This can only be stopped with equipment for regulating the temperature and humidity of the air pumped into the mine.

Complicated technical problems are only part of the matters related to making the headings secure. The saving of the old mine must be joined by scientists from different, perhaps very diverse fields of knowledge. To find a common plane, to devise a common language for art historians and miners is not easy, if it is possible at all. This is attested to by the activities of the Council for Mine Conservation bringing together experts in these two fields. Among other things, it has made an assessment of all the headings for both their historic value and technical condition, and designated on this basis the parts to shut down and those to save. This body also assesses all works planned for the mine's historic parts.

★

On 9 September 1978 the Salt Mine in Wieliczka was entered — as one of the first items — on the UNESCO world cultural heritage list. The entry's citation reads: "The Wieliczka ancient salt mine is the only mining object in the world active without stop since the Middle Ages till the present time. Its genuine and original excavations (galleries, incline drifts, exploitation chambers, lakes, shafts) 300 km. long situated on 9 levels going 327 m. down illustrate all stages of mining technique development in separate historical epochs. The unique collection of mining constructions, installations, implements and tools inside the mine is presenting the systems of salt deposits exploitation and drainage, the mine ventilation and lighting in natural milieu. There are also the relics associated with salt manufactory whose beginning in this area goes back as far as the prehistoric time. The objects of mining art represented by sculptures in salt and the whole underground chapels with rich interior decorations belong to objects without parallel in the world."

Various grades and forms of salt mined at Wieliczka (top from left to right):
fibrous salt, fore-shaft salt, green bed salt, salt crystal, bronze salt, green block
salt also known as stained-glass salt

A cross-section of a silt layer (under the edge of the hammer) and a white salt layer can be seen on the wall of a chamber where green block salt used to be mined. Blocks of salt usually cracked at soft white salt layers

A dolomite salt block

Certain types of bronze salt form colourful patterns on gallery walls

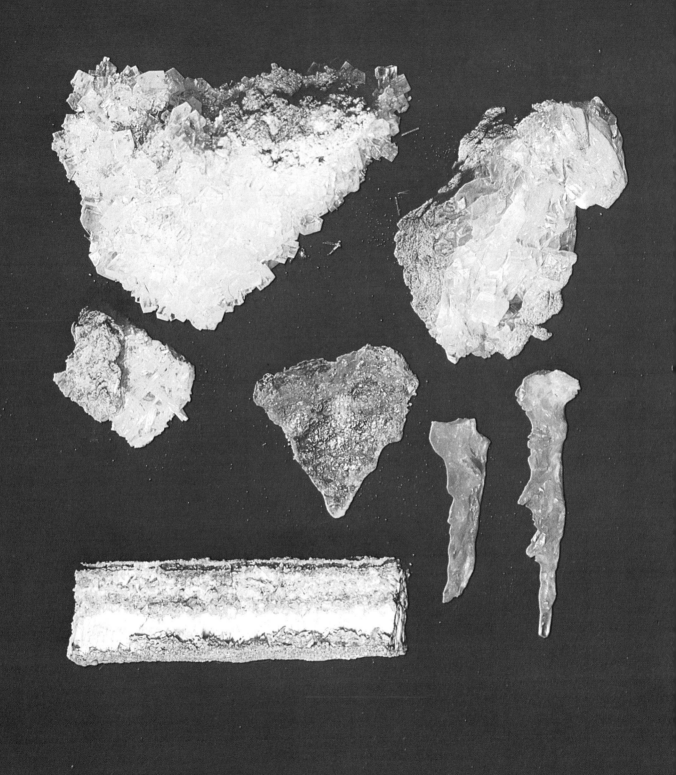

Various forms of gypsum can be found in deposits.
Mirabilite (Glauber's salt) dripstone is shown in the centre

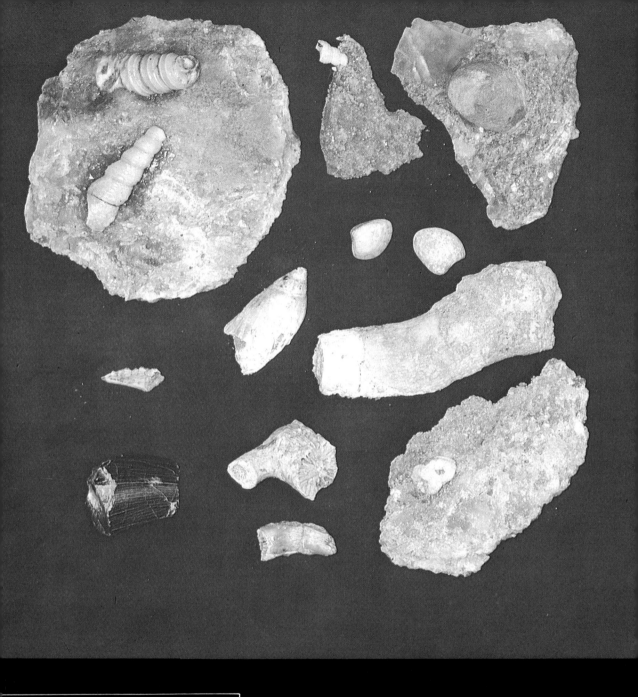

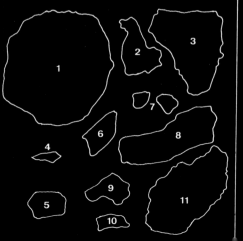

Fossils of animals that lived in the Miocene sea were found during salt mining: 1, 2, 6, 11 — snails; 3 — Bryozoa 7 — clams; 4, 5 — fish teeth; 8, 9, 10 — coral

A carbonized cone stuck in a side wall

A carbonized trunk more than 3 m long, uncovered in the ceiling of a channel

*After the Miocene sea dried out, salt deposits folded due to
orogenic activity in the Carpathians. Brightly coloured
Carpathian flysch can be seen in the gallery wall*

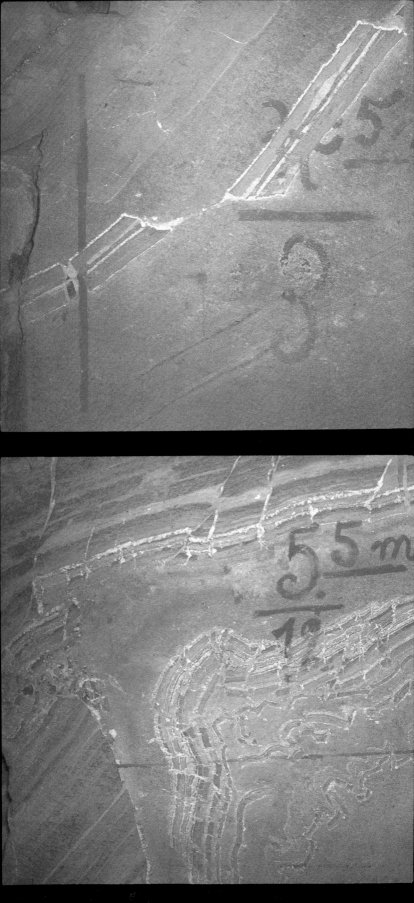

Silt layers in green salt that were broken and displaced due

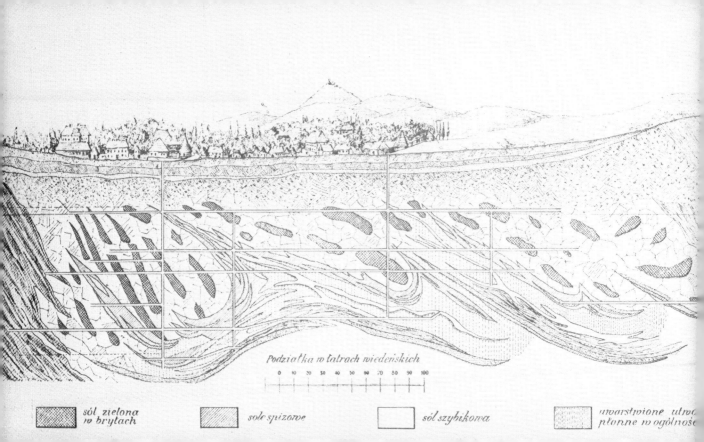

Podziałka w łatrach wiedeńskich

0 10 20 30 40 50 60 70 80 90 100

sól zielona w bryłach   sole spizowe   sól szybikowa   uwarstwione utwory płonne w ogólności

*Various forms of secondary salt crystallization. The brown colour
is caused by iron compounds*

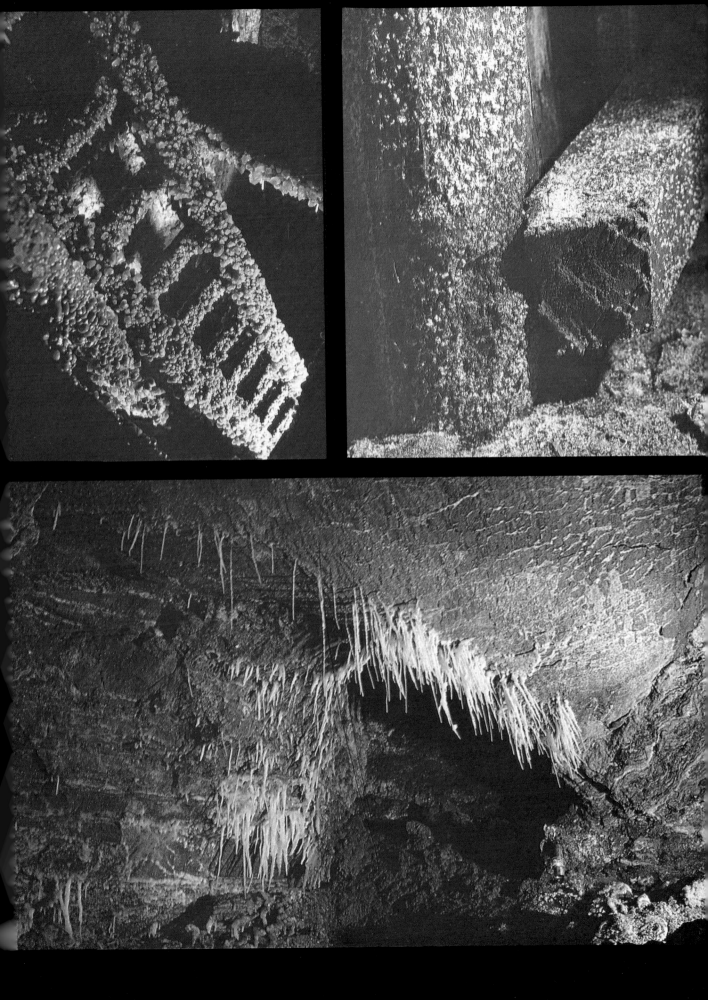

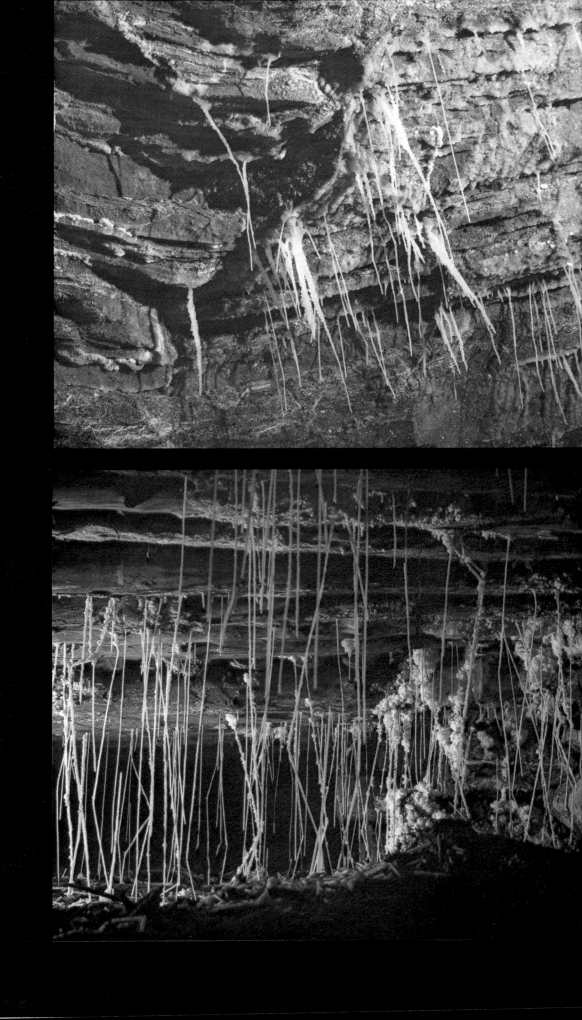

A salt block ready for mining

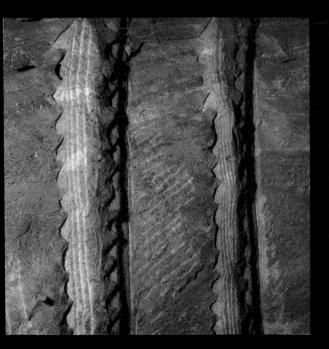

Places where salt blocks were chipped off

Fine fore-shaft salt was extracted from the chamber, while soiled salt folds were left intact.

The compacting of salt in barrels (detail of a 1760 prin by J.F. Nilson drawn according to a 1719 sketch by J.G. Borlach

Particularly difficult was the mining of "eagle" salt found in thin layers, which was designed for the royal court

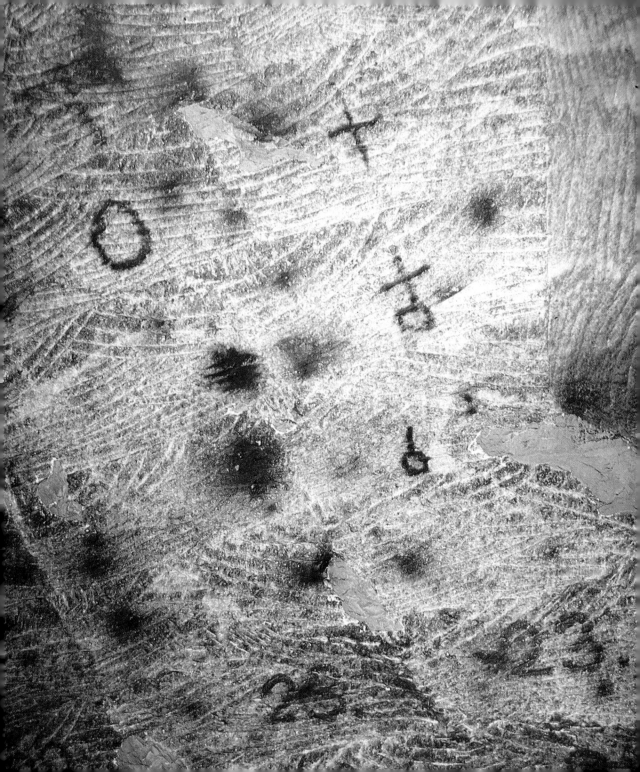

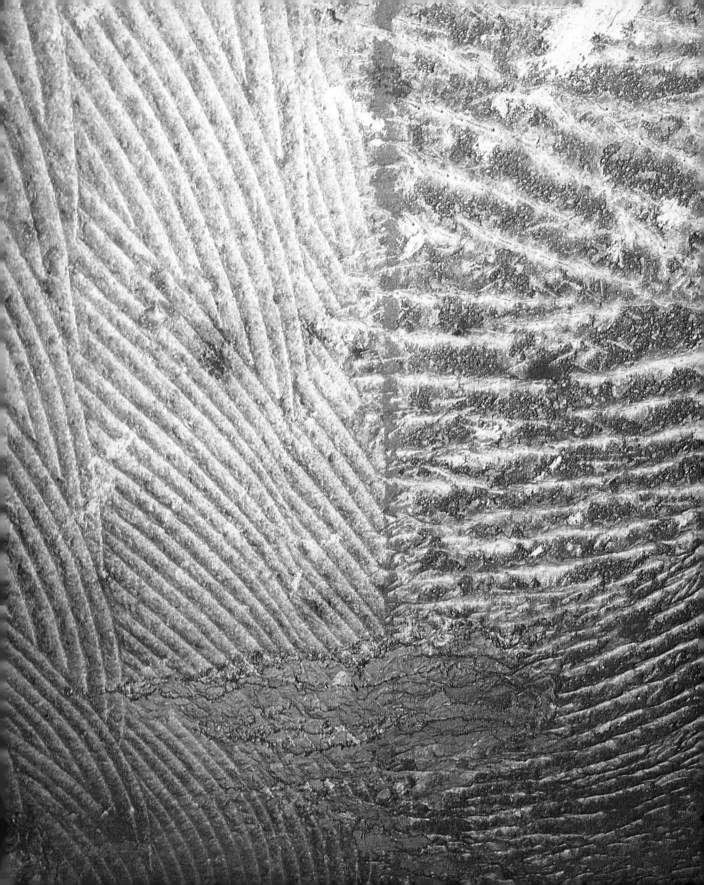

A salt-works master's cross

Characteristic traces made by a cutting machine in a gallery wall

Chambers where salt was mined by spraying

Miners' picks

A hammer and wedges used to loosen salt blocks

A support that protected a miner's back when he carried salt

Shoes that were once discarded under a chamber wall have remained there

*Oil lamps were used to light up galleries in the past
(detail of a 1645 print by W. Hondius)*

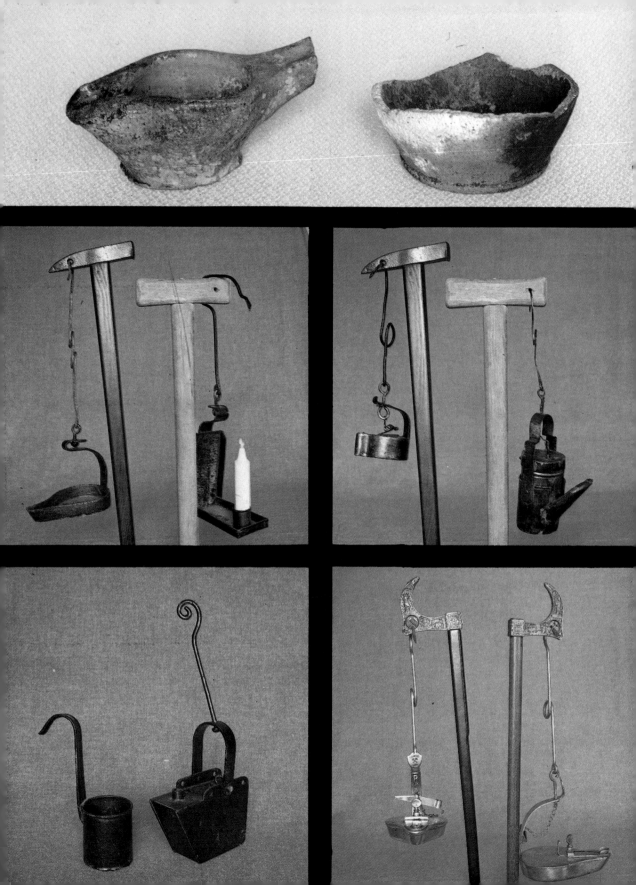

Carbide lamps

Decorated lamps used by mine officials

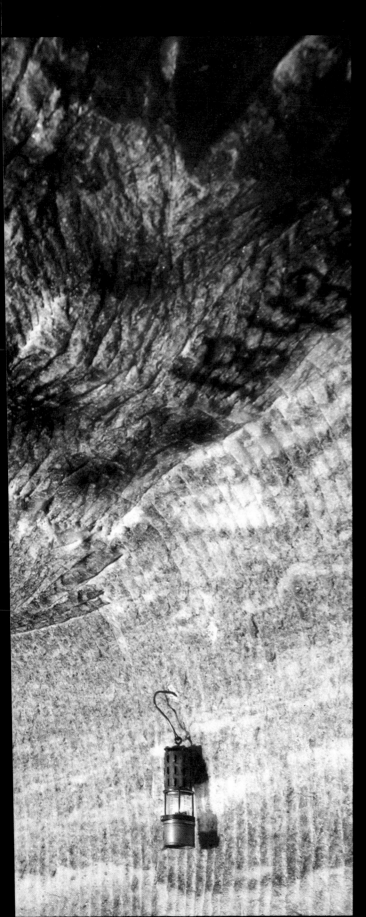

The handling of salt blocks (detail of a 1760 print by J.E. Nilson drawn according to a sketch by J.G. Borlach made in 1719)

A trolley on rails with wooden wheels

Elements of metal trolleys

Windlass. In the foreground: an inclined drift case

A windlass shaft near "Sułów" fore-shaft

The "Eastern Mountains Stable" on the third level of the mine

Stone crib in the "Eastern Mountains Stable"

Saxon horse gear transferred to the Cracow Salt Mines Museum from the "Tworzyjanki" fore-shaft

Hungarian horse gear transferred to the Museum from the "Mirów" fore-shaft

The fastening of a windlass shaft in the "Adamów" chamber

Windlass braking jaws in the "Ciołek" chamber

A roll holding rope over the "Wałczyn" fore-shaft

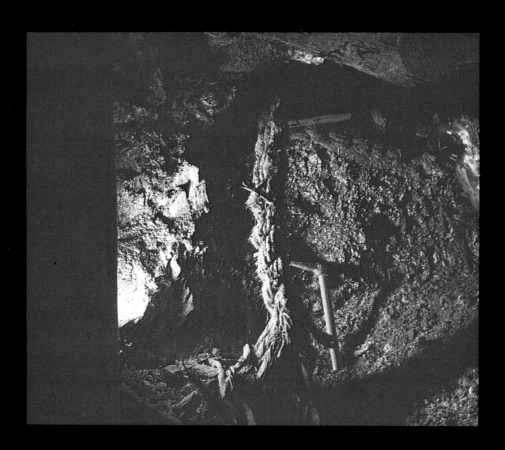

Rope made from lime bark

The "Jakubowice" fore-shaft

Braking equipment

A board into which cogs were stuck to mark the number of blocks extracted from a gallery

Braking equipment

Tanks collecting water drained from headings

Fragments of wooden pipes

A fragment of the "Geisruck" chamber

A fragment of the "Margielnik" chamber

A prop in the "Ksawery" chamber

The construction of a prop; right: the transportation of a salt barrel (a fragment of a 1760 print by J.E. Nilson according to a 1719 drawing by J.G. Borlach)

Limewhited gallery lining — a fire security precaution

A thin salt layer separating the heading from surrounding
silt breaks at a place which is not supported by a prop

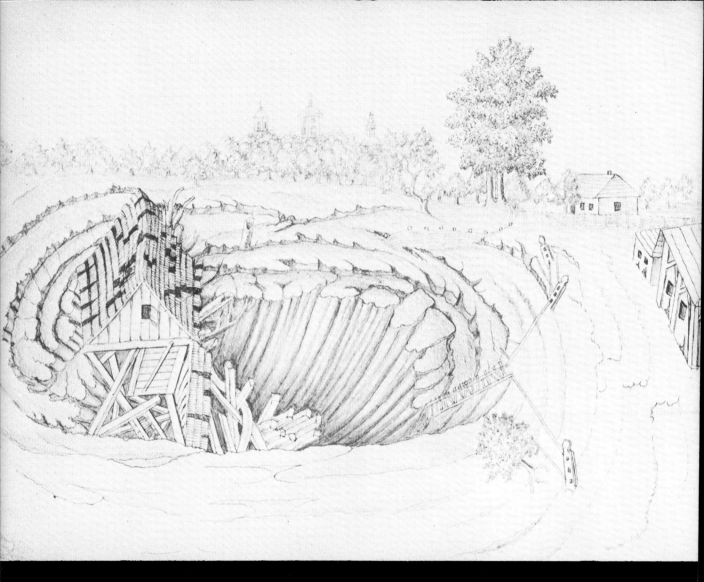

Tree trunks that were used for props were up to 80 cm. in diameter

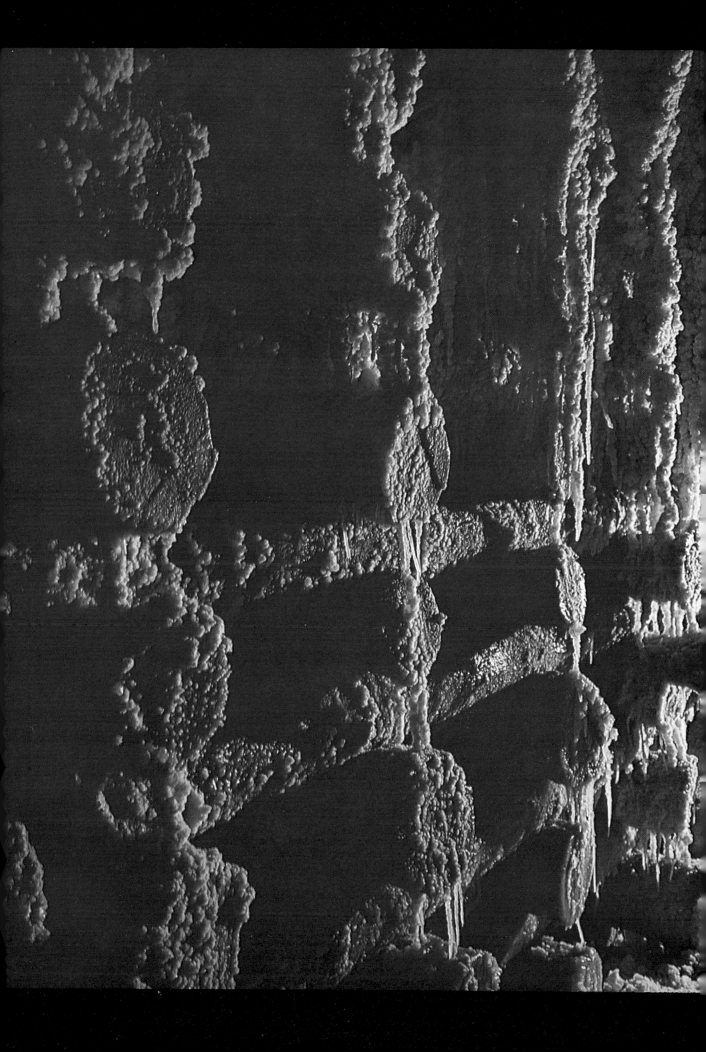

Gallery linings crack under the pressure of rock mas...

Untypical lining of the "Michałowice" chamber

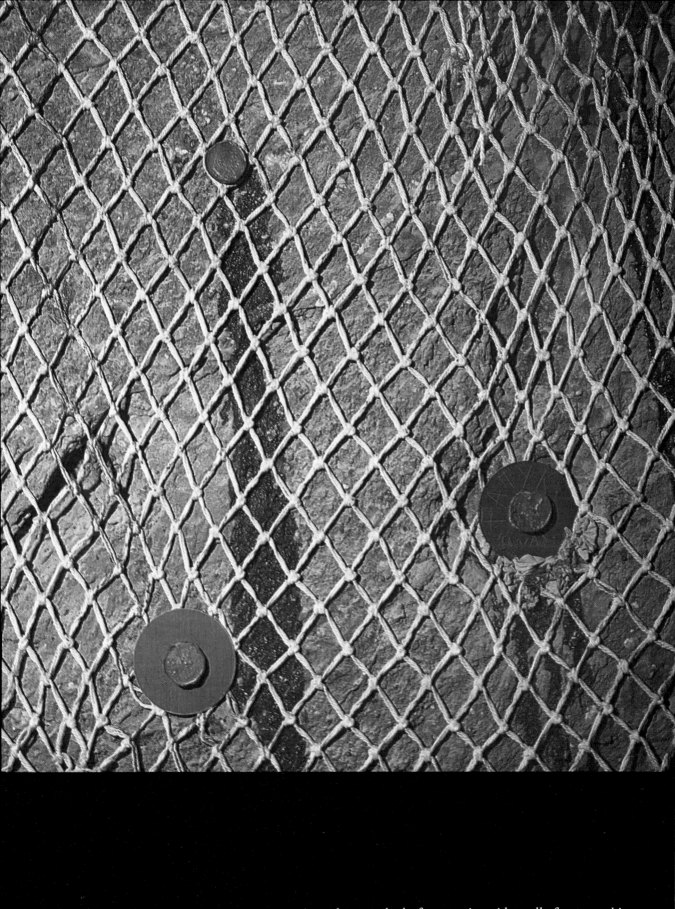

A modern method of preventing side walls from cracking:
a plastic mesh fastened to hooks bonding side walls to rock mass

Delineatio Primae Salisfodinae Wielicensis

WIZERUNK ŻUPY WIELICKEY PIERWSZEY

Professor Alfons Długosz

A horn offered to the miners' guild by Seweryn Boner in 1534

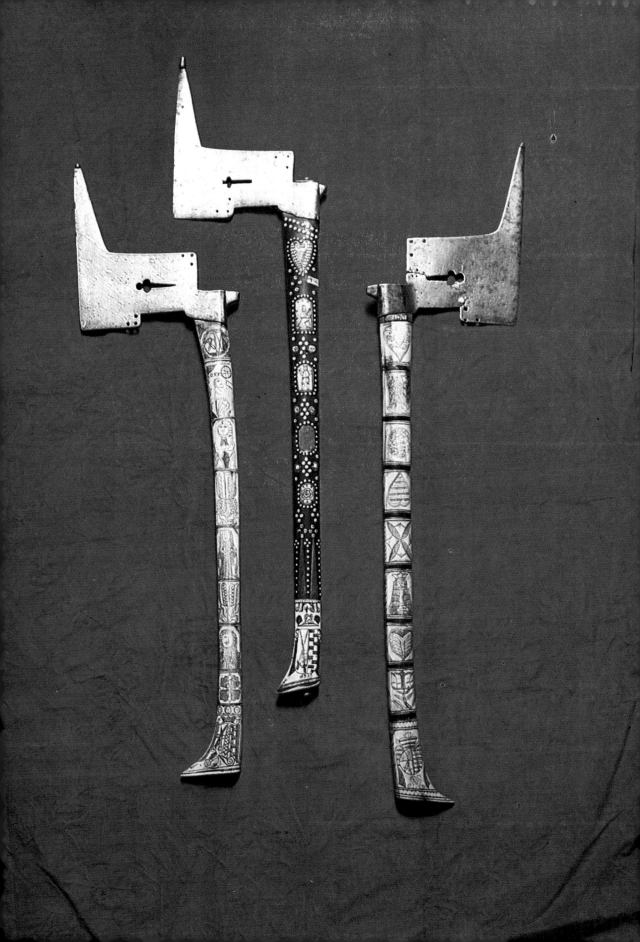

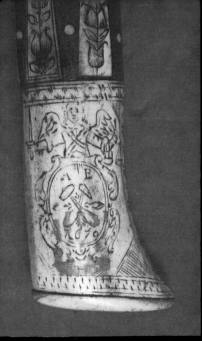

Ceremonial miners'
hatchets

A fragment of a plaque bearing the name of the "Jakubowice" chamber, with an inscription in pencil: "God helps those who call on Him for help"

Symbols and a date chiselled in the side wall, probably a place where a tragedy took place

Some of the signatures down in the mine provoked comments by miners' colleagues. A Wilhelm Małajewicz usually carried a crèche at Christmas. That was why they coined his nickname "Szopa" after "szopka", meaning crèche. They also drew a crèche next to his signatures

St. Anthony's chapel dating back to the late 17th century

*In December 1902 the artist who carved out
the Blessed Kinga's chapel lost two
daughters within a week: 12-year-old Magdalena
and Marysia who was a year older. Their father,
a self-taught sculptor, chiselled their tombstone in sandstone...*

A figure of a kneeling monk can be seen next to a tourist trail. It probably comes from a chapel in the "Boczaniec" which was devastated by fire

*A 17th century figure of the Madonna and Child
in the Holy Cross chapel was transferred from a destroyed
chapel in the "Lizak"*

A chapel in the "Lizak" chamber

A framework chiselled in a salt pillar is what has remained of a chapel

An altar at the crossing of the "August" and "Geramb"
galleries

A chapel in the "Lipowiec" gallery dating back to the 1820s.
The figures are painted with the paint used to mark headings.

A salt pillar with a chiselled framing begins to crack

Tourists visiting the mine (a lithograph from the first half of the 19th century)

The "Gołuchowski Station", a section of a former tourist trail

A section of the "Gołuchowski Station". On both sides of the crossed hammers one can see pale traces in the place from which an inscription "God speed you" was removed in the 1950s

A former ball-room in the "Łętów" chamber, a performance of a "Cracow wedding" for tourists (a drawing by M. Seykotta from the mid-19th century)

"Lake Wessel", a chamber that was to be opened to the
public shortly before World War I

An underground sanatorium,
the chamber named after ar Feliks Boczkowski

A plan of Wieliczka by Marcin German shown on a print by W. Hondius dating back to 1645

St. Sebastian's larch wood church dating back to the 16th century

The Blessed Kinga and Boleslaus the Chaste, a 1907 polychromy by Włodzimierz Tetmajer, can be seen on the ceiling of St. Sebastian's church

A part of the castle — the "House among the salt-pans"

Turówka building

Present state of the mine

Translated by Rafał Kiepuszewski
and Wojciech Worsztynowicz
Graphic design by Hubert Hilscher
Production editor: Wiesław Pyszka
Photographs through courtesy of
the Jagiellonian Library, the National Museum
(the Szołajski Collections, the Czartoryski
Library) in Cracow, and the Museum
of Cracow Salt Mines at Wieliczka.
The photograph of Professor A. Długosz is
a private property of Mr. J. Grzesiowski

This book appears also in French, German, Russian
and Polish

This is the two thousand two hunded and thirty-second
publication of Interpress